Cover illustration by Pen Mendonça www.penmendonca.com. Dr.Pen Mendonça is an independent and pioneering graphic facilitator with twenty years experience of working across the UK public and voluntary sectors, and directly with communities. Her PhD (Central Saint Martins) developed the concept of Values-Based Cartooning, and applied it to a study of single pregnancy / early first-time single motherhood. Pen is an associate lecturer in contextual and theoretical studies, her graphics are widely published, and her essays can be found in Studies in Comics, Women: A Cultural Review and Demeter Press books on motherhood.

Title: Going it Alone: a Guide for Solo Mums in the UK
Author: Emily Engel
Date: July 2019
ISBN: 978-1-78926-720-4
Production: Ingram Spark,

# Going it Alone:

## A Guide for Solo Mums in the UK

Emily Engel

# CONTENTS

## Acknowledgements and Thanks

First of all, I must thank the DIY mums – Elaine, Ros, Pam, Ruth, Gwyneth, Jenny, Nicola, Maggie, Sally, Lorraine, Sasha, Celia, Gabrielle, Kris, Wendy and 'Cilla and all those who have been involved since I first joined in 1991. Without you, I'd have never survived the hurdles that donor conception put in my way over the years of trying. The mutual support and getting to know your lovely kids was the best antidote, and continues to be an important reference point in my life!

I took on the role of co-ordinator for single women in the Donor Conception Network (DCN) in the late 90s. Until 2015 I had the privilege of welcoming most of the new (single) joiners and offering support and information to those who had queries. I facilitated discussion groups at most national meetings until 2015, and co-facilitated many Talking and Telling workshops for single women and lesbian couples.

I owe a debt of thanks to every one of you who has consulted, confided and helped me explore all aspects of this subject and kept me interested and aware of the differences as well as the common ground. I continue to believe, and see the proof again and again, that single women can absolutely provide an environment where our children can thrive and become happy and well-adjusted people. Solo motherhood is not an easy option, but be reassured that there are plenty of us who have gone before you and are happy to share what we've learnt and to help in whatever way we can.

The quotes and examples I have provided all come from interactions with DCN members, in person, over the phone and by email, and the surveys to which you have kindly contributed. As far as possible, I have used the name / pseudonym provided, but in many cases I had none, so have used 'anon'.

I must state clearly that the quotes and personal stories do not always represent my own views or experience: the most important thing I have learned is how diverse we are as individuals. I want this book to address as many of us as possible, so I have included quotes from different perspectives. Please consider kindly and make up your own mind!

A special mention must go to Jane Mattes, Mikki Morrissette and Wendy Kramer in the USA, whose work inspired me to produce this book, hoping I can address the issues as they affect us in the UK. I also have to offer apologies for the areas I have not given the space they deserve – the regions and the needs of minority groups, which I simply did not have the resources to cover properly. I hope that I will get some feedback from the readers to fill these gaps when this book is updated.

Specific thanks need to go to Rita Ferris-Taylor, Tamsin Mitchell and especially to Beth Cox, Pippa Curtis and Ruth Talbot, who provided editorial advice, proof reading and support as well as helping me organise my thoughts and manage my struggles with modern technology.

All remaining flaws and mistakes are my own. I will appreciate your feedback so that future imprints can be improved – send to **solomumsthebook@gmail.com.**

Emily, July 2019

# Terminology, Glossary, Abbreviations and Acronyms

## Terminology

Solo mums: After a few years of co-ordinating the information and activities for single women in the Donor Conception Network, I thought I would sound out the feelings about the different ways of describing ourselves. Women often said they did not choose to be single and did not like that implication in the term 'Single Mother by Choice'.

Many alternatives were suggested, and respondents were asked to explain their preferences. The outcome was clear: over 70% of women liked the term 'solo' best because it tends to be used in positive situations-solo artists, performers and aviators etc.

So if you wondered why I chose it, that's the story!

## Glossary

Anonymous donors: are those about whom the children will never have a right to information.

Blastocyst: When an egg and sperm first fuse, they are called a zygote; once it becomes a ball of cells with an outer layer, it becomes a blastocyst - within the first week, and ready for implantation.

Dibling: a conflation of donor siblings preferred by some – half-siblings also covers children who share one parent but not from donor gametes, so can be confusing.

Donor offspring: babies born of donated gametes become children and then adults - 'donor offspring' includes all age ranges.

Double donation: egg and sperm are both donated and then fertilized for implantation. The donors have no connection with each other, and the embryo is created specifically for you.

Egg-sharing: this scheme is offered at some clinics, where women under 35 needing fertility treatment may offer half the eggs collected for donation in exchange for free or discounted treatment and / or a short cut to the top of the waiting list.

Embryo donation: this is usually where embryos are frozen after fertilisation, and their owner(s) later decide not to use them themselves. The donor(s) may be undergoing fertility treatment with their own gametes or using donated gametes. In this situation, your child may have full siblings growing up in a family with one or both genetic parents.

Gametes: a collective noun to include sperm and eggs (once they've fused together, they become a zygote).

ID release donors: donors whose identity will be made available at a specified time to the recipient and / or offspring.

Known donors: donors whose identity you know at the time of donation.

Private donors: donors who donate outside the regulated system, maybe through organisations that protect their anonymity, or who are recruited from friends, family or otherwise privately. In the latter case, the treatment may take place in a licensed clinic, but otherwise, it will be managed at home or abroad.

## Abbreviations and Acronyms

2ww: the two week wait between treatment and confirmation by pregnancy test - also known as the roller-coaster!

A&E: Accident and Emergency

CMV: Cytomegalovirus

DCN: Donor Conception Network

DCR: Donor Conceived Register

DI: Donor Insemination, i.e. insemination of donated sperm into the vagina to make its own way through the cervix and uterus to the egg.

DSL: Donor Sibling Link

DSR: Donor Sibling Registry

FET: Frozen Embryo Transfer. Embryos that have been frozen and stored from an earlier treatment cycle are transferred to the uterus for implantation.

HCG: Human Chorionic Gonadotrophin
HFE: Human Fertilisation and Embryology

HFEA: Human Fertilisation and Embryology Authority or Act

ICSI: Intra-Cytoplasmic Sperm Injection. The egg is extracted and a single sperm is injected into the egg for fertilization and re-insertion into to the uterus.

IUI: Intra-Uterine Insemination. The sperm is inserted into the uterus, usually through the cervix, to find its own way to the egg for fertilisation and implantation.

IVF: In Vitro Fertilization. The egg(s) is extracted and fertilized in the lab and allowed to grow before being transferred back to the uterus.

NCT: National Childbirth Trust

NICU: Neonatal Intensive Care Unit

NHS: National Health Service

OHSS: Ovarian Hyperstimulation Syndrome

OPK: Ovulation Prediction Kit

OTR: Opening the Register

PND: Postnatal Depression

SET: Single Embryo Transfer. When many eggs / embryos have been fertilised, the best will be chosen and other viable embryos may be frozen and stored. The UK recommendation is that single embryo transplant is preferred for younger women due to the lower incidence of difficulties in pregnancy and birth, and a maximum of three embryos is set, but other countries may have different limits or none at all.

SMC: Single / Solo Mum by Choice (also 'choice mum')
TAMBA: Twins and Multiple Births Association

TTC: Trying To Conceive

UC: Universal Credit

UKDL: UK Donor Link

# Introduction:
## Single by happenstance, mother by choice.

*With thanks to the late Janice Garfunkel for permission to borrow her words.*

Back in the 1980s (when I was in my thirties) I realised time was getting short for me to start the family I had always assumed I would have. There was no man on the horizon to consider for the role of partner in this enterprise; however, my job in social work at the time meant I was aware of donor insemination as an option. Reaching the decision to take this route and announcing it to my closest friends and my sister brought me a surprising feeling of liberation; I suddenly felt lighter and freer and knew deeply that this was the right thing for me. I spent a year or two trying to get other issues in order, mainly housing, and eventually decided I had better just get a move on. In January 1991, I finally made the call to the clinic and set off on the long road that led to where I now sit.

Luckily, I didn't have to make the journey alone. In 1990, a woman called Cilla had asked the clinic staff if she could put up a notice to see if any other single women wanted to meet up. The counsellor said she did not think others would be interested, they were independent, private, and dealing with it by themselves, getting on with their own lives, but she was welcome to try. Cilla put up her notice anyway.

Within weeks, three women met up, and within a year, a steady group was meeting monthly. Twenty-five years on, we still get together regularly. Although many of our children have moved on, they have benefitted from knowing each other throughout their childhood, knowing they were not unique or alone, and forming some good friendships along the way. When the group became too big to meet in each other's houses, a second group formed. We needed names to distinguish the two groups, and as one of the children had referred to us as the DIY group, we stuck with that. There are now numerous groups meeting regularly in the London area and other groups across the country.

My journey to motherhood took three years, thirty cycles of treatment (plain and simple cervical insemination with donor sperm), and two miscarriages. If it had not been for the support of the DIY group, I would never have had the resilience to endure it. But, month after month, I was seeing them become mothers and my hope and determination were reinforced. My son was born in 1995, a sunny (though sleepless) baby confirming that my perseverance had been worthwhile.

I sought out other sources of support – the Donor Conception Network (DCN) in the UK and Single Mothers by Choice (SMC) in the USA, but the active support of the DIY group is the only reason I can write this now.

Although the books from the USA, by Jane Mattes (1), Mikki Morrissette (2) and Louise Sloan (3), are thorough and wide ranging, there are aspects of the culture on the other side of the Atlantic that don't match the situation here. In particular, the lack of nationalised health provision and the general assumption that government interference or regulation is a bad thing, lead to some important differences between the USA and the UK approach.

This book was brewing at the back of my mind for many years, but only recently have I found time to write it. I wanted to offer others a sense of community, hope and potential, which may help overcome the hurdles of creating a family without a partner. This is a UK guide, but I am aware that my perspective may be London-centric, and people in other parts of the UK, particularly in Northern Ireland, Scotland and Wales, may find differences. Fertility treatment will continue to advance, and the choices people make to create their families will continue to evolve. I am hoping this book can grow to include significant differences and changes as they become clear.

Most of this book focuses on using fertility services to start a family because that is my experience and the area least covered in existing books. However, all the sections on raising our children apply equally to all of us who have chosen to start a family on our own, whether that is by assisted conception, adoption or fostering.

> *I have to say that I don't know any women who 'wanted' to do this alone. All the lone / solo parents I know would have loved to have had a partner to do it with, male or female, it's just that life didn't work out like that for us.*
>
> *Anon*

Many women have protested that the terms 'single mother by choice' or 'choice mum', which have become common in the US, do not feel right. Women who have chosen this route have not necessarily chosen to be single, in fact they have often tried hard to find a partner. In recognition of the negative connotations around the term 'single mother'.

I wondered if we could find a better name for ourselves. I carried out a survey of various different options and the term 'solo mum' won by a large margin. Solo is used in positive situations – solo artists and performer, solo aviators and explorers – so that's the term I've used in this book.

Recognising that everything I write will be obsolete in due course, I am depending on you the readers, to let me know what's changing or what is already different. The book is introduced by a website: www.goingitalone.me.uk. and a private discussion forum. All comments, contributions, suggestions and discussion welcome, please contact me for an invitation on solomumsthebook@gmail.com.

I hope you find what you need in this book to help you make the decisions that are right for you, and to reach your goals with confidence and clarity. I just need to re-state that the decisions and goals may change as you go through the process, so be prepared to stand back and re-evaluate, try not to get too fixed about how you will reach them. One of the biggest and hardest, but also most thrilling changes that a family brings to your life is the every-day surprises, the realisation you only have so much control and if you are too set in your expectations, you could miss some of the delights that come your way.

We need to adjust the assumptions made in much research on child welfare to reflect the social changes of the last century. The convention has been twofold: to assume that the traditional family was best, and to blame mothers for any problems arising. The research on families of women who have chosen solo mothering shows little significant difference, though outside the Cambridge Family Research Unit, it has not led to many academics noting the existence of these families and differentiating them. The old convention of 'mother blaming' is gradually being adjusted – the concept of the 'refrigerator mother' as being to blame for autistic spectrum disorders has been discredited, but the tabloid cliché 'blame the families' usually means the mother. It is not fathers who are blamed for failing to read bedtime stories to their children or letting them eat crisps for breakfast. Even the absence of men in the family is blamed on the mothers. We have not started to ask men what is stopping them from playing an equal role in child rearing.

I write this book to contribute to this process. I have not gone over ground that is well covered in books about child development and families formed in the conventional way. The contents are based on my experience of my own situation as well as the many discussions and communications I have had with other solo mums and would-be mums, and my view of the issues that often arise. There are different ways of approaching most of the issues you will meet, and there is rarely a simple answer that applies to everyone, that is why it still interests me after so many years!

References

1. Mattes, J.: Single Mothers by Choice, Three Rivers Press, 1994
2. Morrissette, M.: Choosing Single Motherhood: the Thinking Woman's Guide, Be-Mondo Publishing, 2005
3. Sloan, L.: Knock Yourself Up: No Man? No Problem? Avery, 2007

# Chapter 1: Looking back, and where we stand now

## 1.1 A history of single mothering

The standard belief in Western culture is that the conventional nuclear family set up is 'natural' – a biological imperative, but when you look at it objectively it is not that clear cut. Although pair bonding, monogamy and nuclear families have existed for centuries and in many different cultures, they are certainly not the only shape that families have taken.

In the history of the human race, there are examples of many varieties of social structures – matriarchal and patriarchal, nuclear and extended families, polygamy, polyandry, serial monogamy and so on. Surrogacy is mentioned in the Bible, for example with Bilhah bearing children for Rachel and Jacob. This suggests that there is no single biological imperative determining family relationships, but that different contexts lead to different set-ups developing and working successfully, or becoming obsolete.

In recent history, changes in the economic and social climate eventually led to amendments to UK family law. As standards of living improved, the need to exclude 'illegitimate' children from a claim to inheritance waned. The First and Second World Wars led to a large increase in the number of children born outside marriage. However, the Bastardy Act was not fully repealed until 1987, illustrating the lag between social and legal changes.

Until the twentieth century, women were seen primarily as dependent, first on their paternal families and then on their husbands. The First World War led to greater numbers of women working for employers outside the home, both to keep industry going and to maintain the family income. Women's rights to property, the vote and equal opportunity were legalised over the following decades, thanks to the tireless work of the suffrage movement (3).

After the First World War, the National Council for the Unmarried Mother and Her Child was set up to address the severe disadvantage faced by women left to raise their children alone. The fact that many of them would have married if their partners had survived the war meant that they were now recognised as 'deserving', and should not have to end up in the workhouse where they would be subject to inhumane and dangerous living conditions and be put to forced labour along with their children. Housing, health and education resources were developed in poorer areas, which became the building blocks for the welfare state which was set up after the Second World War by the Beveridge Report.

In 1970, Tess Fothergill started the first self-help group for lone parents. This became Gingerbread, the charity for single parents. The publicity she generated led to the Finer Report on One Parent Families in 1974, exposing the poverty and disadvantages experienced by children in one-parent families. There followed various moves to improve the situation with financial support (lone-parent supplements) and improved access to welfare assistance, such as nursery places and family support.

Many of these have however been withdrawn or severely reduced - from the eighties onwards as part of the cutbacks in public services, and since 2008, as part of austerity measures. One example is the shift in 1997, when One Parent Benefit was separated from Child Benefit and included as part of Income Support instead. Income Support is means tested, and therefore stigmatised and under claimed. The benefit caps introduced since 2013 have also been exposed as discriminating against single mothers by the courts (4). Benefits changes have often been justified, quite insultingly, as a focus on 'traditional family values'.

Alongside the Welfare and social benefits reductions, the NHS has been undermined by constant restructuring and the Academisation of the state school system has been a parallel process of hidden privatisation. Public and social housing stock provision has been drastically reduced. All the basic resources we grew up taking for granted may not be as accessible to our children in the future. This may mean restricted access to free health care alongside the growth of private care. Although most fertility treatment used by single women comes from the private sector already, most of us will have grown up with an expectation of adequate health care and education as public provisions free at the point of access, which would be there for our children's future needs. We therefore need to make provisions for our children in a way that our parents did not, as well as providing for our own retirement and old age in a way that was not true for most of the last century.

## 1.2 The current situation

In the twenty-first century, there are still many assumptions and prejudices about children in one-parent families, based on outdated ideals. The implication is that unconventional family set ups will have negative consequences for the children. However, research is beginning to distinguish between single parents 'by chance' and 'by choice', and outcomes from the Cambridge Centre for Family Research are indicating very different outcomes for women who have made an active decision to have a child without a partner.

In 2013, 5.6% of all births were registered solely to the mother, though some of these families may nevertheless have two parents (5). In the twenty years up to 2017, the number of single parent families grew by over 15% to 1.78 million, or 22% of all families with dependent children. Nine out of ten of these one-parent families were headed by a woman (6).

Alongside the enormous shift in the way we live, there have been big changes in the role and status of women. Women are now seen as equal members of society, with the right to keep their own name, earn their own income and own their home, or at least sign the lease and take on the mortgage.

> *Having come out of a miserable marriage I decided that one happy parent would be better than two miserable ones. I had gotten to where I wanted to be in my career, was financially stable, had bought a family-friendly home, and decided to become a single parent.*
>
> *Anon*

More and more, women no longer feel obliged to conform to convention and gender stereotypes, whether that is in career choices or family making. The perception of what makes for happy healthy children (and mothers) needs to change with reference to objective criteria rather than obsolete ideals. Women should be able to feel positive about taking action in relation to their circumstances, and not feel guilty for being unable to recreate the fairy tales they grew up with.

While the idealised picture of the family has barely changed in fifty years, the reality is that everyone now knows a family that does not fit the mould – with cohabitation, separation, re-marriage and blended families, as well as single-parent and same-sex parented families. They can see the children in these families thriving at home and at school, and usually recognise that good parenting can happen in lots of different settings.

Parenting has become a less private issue. This may be linked to women being more visible in public life than in the past, and voicing their views and concerns in the media, or because there has been a recognition that the function of raising children ready to meet the needs of our society is too important to keep behind closed doors. Child welfare has become the subject of extensive formal study and speculation, as well as regulation and legislation. Now everyone is entitled to a view on childcare and family life. But the stereotypes and myths live on, and much formal research is tainted by obsolete assumptions (7).

Any woman considering starting a family on her own may find herself having to address outdated views from her family, friends and community. These views are, among other things, that her boys will become delinquents through a lack of discipline and her daughters will become promiscuous teenage mums due to lack of good male role models. They will under achieve and have behaviour problems and ail to become stable productive members of society. This can be a major obstacle, even for women who have good grounds to be confident they can manage the task.

*I decided, having just turned 33 that I wasn't able to guarantee a happy relationship with a partner / husband, but I could try to create a happy family that involved children, something which I knew I would regret deeply if I left it ... and then it was all too late.*

*The idea that someone would then have taken that choice away from me was the deciding step. (Not to speak of huge support from my parents and brothers, and lots of soul searching, reading, researching etc. about what is in the child's best interests).*

*Nina*

I believe that social attitudes will only change when the importance of child rearing and childcare is formally recognised, for instance when men routinely take all the paternity leave available to them, and when pay for working with children reflects greater respect and status. The pressures of machismo will wane and men may feel free to play a more equal part in the caring role, and not fear the ties that come with child rearing. At the same time, parents who are managing alone will be recognised as needing practical support

I am hoping this has clarified the situation as I see it, that in the last thirty years, single women have been making a reasoned and responsible choice to start a family. Much of the research and convention still tell us that this bodes poorly for our children, but the studies that are more objective and untainted by traditional stereotypes are showing more optimistic results. I believe it is important for this unbiased research to be at the forefront of all theorising about families and child welfare, as there is a pernicious tendency to blame women for any issues with child development, and the internalised guilt undermines women across the board and causes real damage to them and their children.

If we fall into believing old myths, we risk repeating the same damaging patterns, feeling inadequate and blameworthy as women and mothers, and raising children who feel less is expected of them due to their disadvantage. If we can stay clear-headed about the impact of social factors on family and child welfare, we will be able to find and consolidate the support we need for stable and successful parenting.

## References


1. www.bionews.org.uk/page_138707.asp
2. www.huffingtonpost.com/wendy-kramer/a-brief-history-of-donor-conception_b_9814184.html?guccounter=1
3. www.gingerbread.org.uk/what-we-do/about-gingerbread/our-history/rightsinfo.org/supreme-court-to-hear-challenges-against-controversial-single-parent-benefit-cap/
4. Fawcett Society: Equality: It's About Time - 150 years of progress, www.fawcettsociety.org.uk
5. www.ons.gov.uk/peoplepopulationandcommunity/birthsdeathsandmarriages/livebirths/bulletins/livebirthsinenglandandwalesbycharacteristicsofmother1/2014-10-16
6. www.ons.gov.uk/peoplepopulationandcommunity/birthsdeathsandmarriages/families/bulletins/familiesandhouseholds/2017#number-of-families-in-the-uk-continues-to-grow-with-cohabiting-couple-families-growing-the-fastest
7. Lamb, M.: Parenting and Child Development in 'Nontraditional' Families, Psychology Press, 1998

# Chapter 2: Choosing to go it alone

*"And the day came when the risk to remain tight in a bud was more painful than the risk it took to blossom".*
Anaïs Nin

## 2.1 Who are the solo mums?

To check out some of the stereotypes about solo mums and to gain a true picture of our make-up, I conducted a survey of single women members of the DCN. The results are collated in appendix 1 at the end of this book.

The survey took place between December 2015 and February 2016 and had 225 respondents. 72% were pregnant or had successfully completed treatment, with 13% considering having a second baby. 25% were still considering or trying to start a family, and 3% had either decided not to proceed or had tried unsuccessfully and then decided to move on. A fuller record of the Survey, with the complete data, is included on the website: www.goingitalone.me.uk

### Age

As expected, most women who choose to become solo mums do so at around the time their biological clock is telling them it's time to get a move on (generally between the ages of 35 and 39). Surprisingly, though, the results showed that some women first considered solo motherhood much younger, even in their early twenties. In these cases there were usually specific reasons. Two women told me their experience of early abuse had led them to this decision before they'd considered any other option. I was equally surprised to find that many women,

15 of them, did not consider solo motherhood until after they reached the age of 40. There could be various reasons for this, but many said they wished they'd better understood the fast decline of fertility.

As expected from these results, the majority of single women giving birth to their first donor-conceived child were between 37 and 43. Only 7% were over 46, of whom three were over 50. We can assume that the women over 45 used donated eggs, unless they were prescient enough to have frozen their own eggs when they were younger, and lucky enough that these thawed successfully.

Nearly a fifth of the women surveyed took less than three months to make the decision to start trying for a baby alone, but nearly a third took over two years to make the leap from thinking to doing.

The Human Fertilisation and Embryology Authority (HFEA) figures for 2014-16 (1) suggest that 26% of treatment cycles result in a live birth. Their figures are usually delayed by the fact that births occur nine months after the registered treatment episode, and it can take several months for births to be notified. This figure includes all types of treatment and patients in all age groups, so it's a very broad average of four cycles of treatment per birth. Cycles of treatment are usually more than one menstrual cycle, so not easily counted in real time.

**Education**

The majority of single women had a first degree; a third also had a master's degree or equivalent. Ten percent had a doctorate or equivalent degree. In this respect, solo mums do seem to match the stereotype of being well-educated.

**Income**

However, well-educated does not necessarily mean well-paid, and single women on this path are a diverse group in terms of earnings. £30-40,000 per annum (pa) was the most common income bracket, closely followed by £20-30,000 pa. 18% of the single women surveyed earn less than £20,000 pa. A similar proportion earned over £60,000 pa. Many in the lowest income group were currently on maternity leave or had chosen to return to work part-time to have more time with their children. A number also made radical career change decisions, re-training so they could work in more family-friendly jobs such as teaching or child-minding.

**Housing**

The majority of women surveyed were homeowners, with 24% owning their home outright. Twelve women were sharing their home. Unsuitable housing was often quoted as the reason to delay starting a family.

**Finances**

Money was a concern for most in some form or other, though 23% reported no financial worries.

**Other dependents**

Many women believed they would become responsible for ageing parents before their children were grown up, with 20% already providing some care or support.

**Conclusions**

The conclusions we can draw from this is that solo mums and those aiming to become solo mums are a diverse group. They have certain things in common, being on average older and better educated than the typical first time mother. Housing and care of ageing parents are often a worry. The stereotype of the 'must have it all' high-flying professional does not apply to most, though the characteristics of decisiveness and resilience are common.

This research is just a snapshot in time, and future research of this nature might show very different results linked to revolutions in treatment options and the changing social context.

## 2.2 The nature vs. nurture debate

When thinking about going it alone, it's important to think about what it means to use donor gametes (sperm and / or egg) and your beliefs about genes and DNA, as well as 'nature' vs. 'nurture', as this will impact your relationship with your child(ren). Ever since Darwin developed his theory of evolution by natural selection, there has been a lively debate between those who believe that your genetic make-up determines who you are and those who believe that your experiences shape you become. In fact, most people now accept that nature and nurture both play an important role, and the debate has moved to arguing over the proportions each of them play, and how and when. You may believe that biology defines you, or you may believe that you are formed by your experiences, or any mixture of the two. What is important is to re-examine these beliefs in light of the family you are considering creating.

A conviction in biological determinism can be problematic for those considering using donated gametes to create a family as it implies that parents have little personal influence on our children beyond passing on our genes. All children present a challenge at one stage of their development or another, so it helps if your beliefs encourage you to 'get it right' and adapt to meet your children's needs, rather than having to accept it as a biological process over which you have no influence. If your children feel less 'yours' because you don't know the origins of their genes, it may feel harder to be confident in your parenting and resist echoes of the 'blood is thicker than water' saying.

For those of us using adoption, it is important to recognise your role in supporting your child to overcome any early disadvantage and not fall into fatalistic views such as that 'bad blood will out', 'sins of the fathers' and the like.

Belief in the influence and importance of 'nurture' means that you can aim to support your children's needs, whatever they are. You can foster an environment where they can grow healthy and strong, emotionally as well as physically. You can also provide the building blocks for healthy relationships even if you can't offer a model of a romantic partnership at home. You can adapt to the circumstances that occur and take responsibility for promoting their well-being. The downside of believing nurture is all is that it can lead to a belief that you have total control over your children and who they become, which is simply unrealistic, and liable to foster guilt if anything goes wrong.

What you can do is work at providing for your children to the best of your ability, in light of your circumstances, give them the freedom to become their own person, and be prepared to accept them and the surprises they offer. A balanced view of the role of genes and nurture will help you to accept the mystery of your children's genetic heritage. Knowing that the environment you provide will be pivotal gives you a responsibility to offer the best that you can.

The science of epigenetics has had a big influence on the nature vs. nurture debate as it shows that 'nurture' in previous generations affects the 'nature' of future ones. Epigenetics is concerned with the way in which genes are switched on or off according to environmental influences. No matter how strongly your genes influence whom you become, they themselves are not immutable, but subject to all sorts of influences (the strongest factors being diet and exercise) even before conception. And it is not just our children who feel the impact, but also future generations. Studies have shown that certain environmental factors, such as famine, have a marked effect on the children of women pregnant at the time, as well as their grandchildren.

The impact of genetics and epigenetics is not always negative, nor a certainty. You may be predisposed to something, but lifestyle will influence whether that predisposition comes to fruition or not (2).

## 2.3 Support needs and networks

Reading and hearing about the experiences of others can also help to answer questions and provide reassurance that this route is a positive option.

The DCN was founded to create supportive networks for those using donor conception. Their website contains a number of useful resources including case studies, a library of books and DVDs, and support booklets. They also run workshops and conferences and have local support groups.

Online material for organisations such as the Infertility Network UK, Fertility Friends, the HFEA, and the specialist organisations in the USA, Choice Moms and Single Mothers by Choice, can also be a useful starting point for reassurance and background reading.

Talk to friends and family and listen to their reactions. You may instantly find a positive response or you may have to tread gently in order to gain their support, they may just need a little time to get used to the idea, or they may have personal beliefs that they need to challenge. Whatever the case, consider your situation: getting pregnant and raising a child (alone or not) is challenging and there will inevitably be times when you feel unsure of yourself and need to rely on the support of others.

> *For the first year I did not discuss it with anyone but just thought through whether I could justify to a child that I brought her into the world knowing that there would not be a father. In the second year, I started to discuss it with a couple of very close friends who were very supportive. I also joined the DCN and went to one of their national meetings. Other women there were very helpful and open and it was inspiring to see them with their children*
>
> *Anon*

Once you start trying to conceive, support can be crucial to help you keep your spirits up. This is when you start seeing yourself in a different light. Fertility treatment can be harrowing and exhausting, and you will be much better off if you can identify ways of getting support. Women who go down the route of solo motherhood tend to be used to being in control.

Relinquishing some of that control and asking for help can be hard. Most likely you have been someone who is responsible and independent, and now you need to acknowledge that you can do this better if you have good support. Although not everyone is interested in joining groups or building networks, everyone will experience times when they need external support. The fact is that fertility treatment can take a long time to succeed and some of the treatments can have difficult side effects; there is a good reason why it is often described as an emotional roller coaster.

Consider your own needs and the sort of person you are:

- Do you need someone to help you talk things through and think clearly?
- Do you need to spill out your emotions to lighten the load, or do you usually mull things over until they become clear?
- Do you find other people's troubles annoying or distracting, or does it help you to know that others have been through it too?

These questions should help you look in the right direction for the support you need. If you want a mutual and personal level of support, see if you can join a support group or contact other would-be solo mums through the DCN or Fertility Friends. If there is no support group in your area you could consider starting one. Your clinic counsellor might also be willing to help by letting other patients know that you are looking to connect.

If a less personal connection works better for you an online forum might be your best option – the main open network in the UK is Fertility Friends. Even when someone else's experience is not much like your own, it may be that a particular event rings bells and helps you face an obstacle. For instance, I have heard several times from women who have agonised over choosing just the right donor but then had repeated failed cycles of treatment. Finally, somebody on a forum has suggested changing the donor, and doing just this has led to success. However, remember that there is a fine line between finding that little nugget that will make it all seem clear and simple, and information overload where the complexity of choices becomes overwhelming and paralysing.

*Friends were positive, but little or no help in practical terms (too busy with jobs / families etc.) when I was ill or desperately needed some sleep. Support structures in terms of people present was very hard to get, especially in an emergency. I'd advise to get friends to commit to providing a few hours of help (cleaning / cooking / minding baby while you sleep) instead of buying baby presents / clothes – that's what would have been much more valuable to me.*

*Sarah Hannah, London*

Building these support networks is great practice for solo mothering, when you will also need to be able to ask for help and solidarity, as well as having back up for emergencies and crises. The simplest things like a chat and cup of tea can alleviate the everyday toil of parenting.

It won't be good for you or for your child if you cannot find help when things get tough, as they inevitably do– when you or your child gets sick, when you feel pulled between your child's needs and another family member's, when work is demanding or some unpredictable challenge crops up. You owe it to yourself to have fall-back plans, your child deserves it too, and you will both feel the more secure and confident for it.

## 2.4 Dealing with negative reactions

The big fear is that at some stage or another you will evoke negative reactions. Your family or someone else who matters might disapprove of your choice (or your 'failure' to provide grandchildren in the usual way), your friends might not support you, and ultimately, that your children might suffer due to the perception of one-parent families in society, or due to some perceived inadequacy in the family you've provided them.

There are two issues here.

- The first is the concern that a non-traditional family will put children at a disadvantage,
- the second is how to deal with any disapproval you might meet.

There is not enough decent research on solo mum families, as most evidence on children in one-parent families is obtained from families where the child was either unplanned, and the father has been uninvolved from the start, or where the parents have separated at a later stage. These scenarios offer quite different environments from single women who have proactively chosen to become solo mothers, and consequently have a different impact on the child. On the whole solo mums are older, have stable living situations and established careers and incomes. This was examined thoroughly in section 2.1 above.

Most women find that those they tell are positive and even enthusiastic about their decision. If you're not confident that this will be the case, the best way to deal with negative assumptions is to pre-empt them by presenting your decision to start a family on your own as a positive and informed choice, made from a position of strength and confidence. On the whole, people will respond to your optimism in the same spirit, and respect you for having made your plans with forethought and consideration for your children. This is a good opportunity to let people know that you will value their support, that you don't imagine you can do it all alone and that you appreciate them. There is no need to make out that everything will be easy, it is much more realistic to acknowledge the challenge, and share your excitement and enthusiasm.

If people voice their fears for your children and that their fate will be that of the 'typical fatherless child', you can gently remind them that there is nobody to blame or resent, or to drain you emotionally, so there is no basis for their concern.

There are numerous different family set ups, and some of us will live in places where we are surrounded by different family types, and can presume that our children will have peers without a dad at home, or in the picture, or peers who are donor conceived for different reasons. Some of us won't find it as easy to be confident in this assumption, either because of the area we live in, or of the specific community to which we belong. In a small community where the majority of families are of a traditional set up or where everybody knows each other's business, it may feel like a bigger risk to go against convention. But remember that all is not always as it seems from the outside, and family situations change and adapt. You may discover that other families have used fertility treatment but never mention it until you do, and you may find also that people take a while to get used to a new idea, just as it took you a while to get round to the decision for yourself.

Some women may fear that the cultures and beliefs of their community may be less accepting and this choice will open them up to condemnation. Ultimately, if you have concerns about how your local community will perceive your family, you need to evaluate whether and how this will affect you and your child. If you can find support so that you can surround your child with love and acceptance, you should be able to counterbalance an unsympathetic environment to a certain extent, though you will also have to make sure you help your child develop their own defences when they become more independent and you're not always there to protect them. In such an environment, there may be a temptation to keep the truth of your child's origins secret but, as discussed in Chapter 6, this is not the best course of action for your child, not least because it tends to undermine relationships with fear, suspicion and distrust.

You might consider moving to find a more supportive environment for your family. After all, people move for the sake of their child for various reasons, such as to be in a good school catchment area or to be closer to family. Respect and acceptance are as crucial for our children's welfare as the right school.

In the case of religious communities, I know several women who looked around within the same faith to find a new church, mosque, temple or synagogue with a more diverse congregation where they felt more welcome. If your child is older and school is an issue, sometimes a different school in the same denomination may be more accepting.

Whatever the case, you can be sure that others have faced the same situation and found a way to move forward. Ask around and find out about others who have met challenges with acceptance and you will be on your way to finding a new support network.

## References


1. www.hfea.gov.uk – as the website is regularly revised, search for 'fertility treatment in year (...). At time of writing, the latest available figuredfs were for 2016. There is usually a 2-year delay in publication to allow for the gap between treatment and childbirth as well as delays in reporting.
2. www.whatisepigenetics.com/fundamentals/

# Chapter 3: Choosing donor conception

*"The goal of a single parent is not to raise our children alone. The goal is to consciously create the village in which we and our children will thrive."* Mikki Morrissette, founder of Choice Moms, author 'Choosing Single Motherhood: the Thinking Woman's Guide'

This chapter looks specifically at choosing assisted conception to become a solo mum. The option of adoption will be considered separately in Chapter 5.

## 3.1 A brief history of assisted conception

The world of assisted conception is changing all the time, with new issues coming up as it evolves. Fertility has always been of fundamental importance in society, with the perpetuation of the human race being seen as a basic human function.

There are records of donor insemination from the eighteenth century showing that assisted conception has been practised for longer than we generally acknowledge. In America at the end of the nineteenth century, Dr William Pancoast inseminated a woman with donor sperm while she was anaesthetised, without her knowledge, but with her husband's consent (1). The fact that donor conception was hidden in secrecy and shame meant that the practice was not subjected to open scrutiny, and therefore often lacked basic ethical consideration. By the middle of the twentieth century, donor insemination was being made available to infertile couples in several clinics in the UK, but it was still unregulated and unpublicised for fear of negative reactions. It is believed that sperm was often collected from the doctors involved, or their students and colleagues (2).

The first IVF pregnancy succeeded in 1978, and led to a growing realisation that regulation and guidance were needed. However, the Human Fertilisation and Embryology (HFE) Act was not passed until 1990. Since then, technology has improved greatly, although there are still many unknowns. Simple cervical insemination has largely been replaced by intra-uterine insemination, and there is wider use of drugs and scans to control and monitor ovulation.

The widespread use of Intracytoplasmic Sperm Injection (ICSI), where a single sperm can be injected into the egg, means that many of the heterosexual couples who would previously have needed to use donor sperm can now achieve a pregnancy with their own gametes (egg and / or sperm). The technology of egg and embryo storage has also allowed many more women to benefit from assisted conception if they have had or are at risk of early menopause or other medical conditions that compromise their fertility, or because they are single or in lesbian relationships.

**3.2 Is donor conception right for you?**

Single women considering assisted conception usually put in a great deal of forethought. Even if the initial decision is made hastily, it takes considerable commitment to follow it through.

> *The decision to go it alone was very difficult for me, like giving up on 'the dream', but the need to be a mother was much stronger.*
>
> *Ellie (age 41), Derby, mum to a baby boy*

Fertility treatment can be an arduous process, and with limits on NHS funding, most women have to use the private sector and incur significant costs. Aside from finances and fertility treatment, it is important to consider how the choices you make now will affect your future child and how your child might feel about their origins. Having support is also critical for yourself, as well as for your child's welfare, whether on a day to day basis or in a crisis.

> *Two of my friends broke up with long-term boyfriends and had a fertility panic and went for tests to try to gauge how fast the clock was ticking. I had also just broken up with my boyfriend, and although 'only' 32, thought 'Wouldn't it be better to know at 32 than at 38?' so I went for the same fertility MOT. Their results were great. Mine was not. I had the average levels of a 42 year old and not a 32 year old.*
>
> *The doctor said 'You should consider having a baby by yourself' – it had honestly never crossed my mind before.*
>
> *Nina (age 33)*

Most women considering solo motherhood begin to do so some time in their mid to late thirties (when their fertility is thought to start its decline). Some will reach this point when they are younger – perhaps because they don't want to wait any longer, perhaps because of risk of early menopause, or because they don't have any interest in finding a partner. Whatever the reason, they may find themselves trying to justify making this choice before they seem to have given the 'conventional' option a fair chance.

Women who identify as lesbian and bisexual may have already begun to consider the necessity of using donor sperm for conception regardless of their family set up but, as with heterosexual women, find themselves single when they are ready to have children, so go ahead alone.

> *I had three significant relationships before I finally made the reluctant decision that I had to just get on with it regardless of what my partner felt.*
>
> *I really wanted the baby to be ours but said she was ambivalent and always said that it wasn't her decision. When the baby did actually come she freaked out, and after quite a tough first year of the baby's life we split as partners.*
>
> Anon.

Even once the decision has been made, it's not unusual to have moments of hesitation. Moving forward may involve abandoning long-held dreams of the ideal relationship and family, and facing anxiety about what donor conception could mean to a future child.

Psychoanalysts will say that the absence of a partner is a loss that needs to be grieved before a solo mother can proceed, and this may be the case for some women, especially if they have had relationships which they thought might lead to children. However, loss and sadness should not be seen as defining characteristics of solo mums,

Many others, myself included, will never feel such a loss, or will not feel it strongly. Rather than a loss, I felt disenchantment with the fantasies of the fairy-tale life presented to me in childhood. The disillusionment started in my teens, in the 1960s, when I began to want more for myself than life as a mother and housewife. By the time I was in my thirties, I knew much more about the alternatives to the 1950s' ideals I had grown up with and was eagerly living my life according to the new rules. It was without any regret that I decided to have a family on my own, rather than to compromise with Mr Good Enough.

Whatever process you have gone through leading up to this point, choosing this route may be felt as liberating and empowering; many of us celebrate not feeling bound by traditional expectations and obsolete prescribed roles.

It is important to address any emotional obstacles before moving forward. Mothers, especially single mothers, can come in for a hard time from the media. It's necessary to consider your own vulnerability to blame and guilt, and to acknowledge your limitations. Having wanted to create the ideal childhood for your child, you may feel guilty when things are tough. But there are aspects of the world, and your child's life, which are way beyond your control. Rather than striving for impossible perfection, foster the skills and attitudes that will help your child face challenges and adversity with confidence, creativity and resilience. Of course you must protect them as far as you can, but help them also to learn to assess situations, face risks and uncertainty and make considered choices and decisions. The issue of fostering resilience in children is dealt with in detail in Chaptter 8.

To check out your own personal beliefs, consider:

- What your thoughts are on nature vs. nurture and the influence of genetic make-up.
- How would you feel about only having limited information about your child's genetic background?
- What are your beliefs about what makes a family?

- How do you feel about building an unconventional family and providing everything your child needs yourself?
- How will you answer to those who challenge your family set-up?

If you feel uncertain, indecisive or hesitant, for example if you firmly believe that our genetic make-up determines who and what we are, or that a child needs two parents, or a parent of each gender, you need to think carefully before you continue. It may help to talk these issues through with a counsellor who can help you reflect on where your assumptions come from and whether they still hold true for you, or might be holding you back. Our belief systems are often complex and rooted in our culture and upbringing, but people can and do change their beliefs when they are incompatible with the reality they face. If you find some clarity regarding your personal beliefs and your reasons for them, you will feel stronger and more able to move forward.

Women who take this route usually receive favourable reactions and it is essential to ensure that solo motherhood is chosen as a positive option that can be upheld with confidence. Not only for any critics you might face, but also to a future child questioning and challenging you about their origins. This confidence will be your main defence against the undermining pressures of doubts and stereotypes; if you can stand proud and announce your decision and family status with delight and pride, people are likely to respond in kind, with respect and support.

## 3.3 Getting ready for treatment

You can prepare yourself for treatment in several practical ways. Routine health and fertility checkups are available through a GP, and unless you hope to be referred for NHS treatment, you don't have to tell your GP how you plan to conceive. However, this can be a good opportunity to raise the subject. Although your fertility treatment may not involve your GP, you will eventually need them when it comes to antenatal care and care for your baby, so their support could be reassuring. If you do not get a positive reaction from them, you will have time to seek out a more receptive doctor. Some women have found particularly supportive GPs who have been willing to carry out some of their blood tests, avoiding the charges in private fertility clinics.

There are several excellent guides to take you through the preparation for fertility treatment and pregnancy. Check your local library to compare what each book offers before you buy, as they each have their own style. Toni Weschler (3) is particularly good on learning to read your body's signs.

**Getting to know your cycle**

Familiarity with your menstrual cycle will help when it comes to getting pregnant. Tracking your cycle and Basal Body Temperature (BBT) can be helpful, as well as looking for other signs of ovulation, including changes in your cervical fluid. Ovulation prediction kits (OPKs) can also be used. There are various websites and apps to help with charting all this information.

**Weight**

Hormones and fertility are closely linked to weight. Being over or underweight can affect your chances of getting pregnant, and if your body mass index (BMI) is not within a healthy range, your clinic may insist that you remedy this before starting treatment. Energy, stamina and mobility are essential as a new mother, so it's worth considering how your weight will affect this as well. This is a time when many issues linked to our expectations and femininity may need to shift. If you've had difficulty maintaining a healthy weight or resisted the pressure to conform, you may need extra support with this. This is about preparing your body for a pregnancy and a healthy baby, s0 it's important to move on from any underlying fears that may be in the way.

**Supplements**

There are a myriad of recommendations for fertility and pregnancy nutrition. Given the survival of the human race so far, it's likely that an all-round balanced and healthy diet should suffice, but do read up if you feel you need to boost your health and fitness with manufactured supplements. Be aware that this is a lucrative business, so check the commercial links of whoever's advice you are taking!

> *I always knew that not being a mum was a situation*
> *I never wanted to find myself in. I kept hoping that*
> *I would meet someone and have a family conventionally.*
> *I had decided that by the age of 38 I would go it alone...*
> *I started reading, putting myself on a supplement*
> *and lifestyle plan for women with fertility issues,*
> *and started my treatment at age 39. I was successful*
> *on my first IVF cycle and I have five embryos frozen!*
> *Anon.*

Women need to increase their intake of folate several months before they conceive. Eating leafy green vegetables and taking a supplement can reduce the risk of spinal defects in your baby. Folic Acid is the artificial form of folate, providing the B9 that is in leafy green vegetables (4).

**Budgeting**
Fertility treatment is expensive and a child will make financial demands on you for 18 years at least. Investigate the local cost of childcare as well as fertility treatment. Look at your monthly expenditure and see where you can cut costs and make savings.

*The main factor that is hindering me is money. I feel that I need to be in a better financial position.*
*At the moment I do not have the money for treatment.*
*Anon.*

If you can start saving money as soon as you've taken the decision, this will form a nest egg should you need it – perhaps for unexpected treatment costs or a deposit for a childcare place, or all sorts of incidentals later on. Changing your spending habits and saving in this way will help you adapt more easily to life as a solo mother.

## 3.4 Choosing a fertility clinic

Choosing a fertility clinic can be fraught. Most fertility treatment happens in the private sector and the options regarding types of treatment, reputation, success rates, cost and location may seem confusing and daunting. To complicate things further, there is also the option of going to a clinic overseas.

*I asked my doctor to refer me to a certain clinic in London as this was the closest clinic to my home. I had not even considered that I might get treatment on the NHS. I went along to the first consultant appointment with my cheque book and almost fell off my chair when she said she would like to offer me 3 'attempts' at intrauterine insemination (IUI) on the NHS. Luckily for me I got pregnant first time!*

*Anon*

NHS funding for fertility treatment is scarce and can be a postcode lottery. Although there are guidelines, each area's Clinical Commissioning Group (CCG) has discretion over the provision they offer, including how many cycles of treatment and the eligibility criteria. Age restrictions exclude many women who have decided to go it alone and some health trusts will only fund women with a diagnosed fertility problem. The Fertility Fairness website (5) has up to date details of IVF treatment offered by each CCG and further details, including intrauterine insemination (IUI) provision, can be found on your CCG website. If you are lucky enough to get NHS funding, you will be referred by your GP. If you live somewhere where there is a choice of clinics, you can often state your preference, so the information on choosing a clinic will still be relevant.

In the UK the regulatory body, HFEA, sets the required standards, inspects, and licenses fertility clinics. The HFEA provides enormous amounts of information about the activities and performance of all UK fertility clinics from their inspections and has a very useful 'Choosing a Fertility Clinic' tool (6).

*I very much anticipated [discrimination] but my experience with my clinic was great. After all, single women and lesbians make up a big proportion of their customers!*

*Anon*

Success rates are hard to compare due to the variety of different practices and client groups across clinics, so start identifying the factors that are most important to you and make a priority list or even a spreadsheet to help you choose. The criteria might include size, distance, accessibility, waiting lists, prices, choice of donors, range of procedures available, evening and weekend opening times, proportion of other patients in your age group / needing the same procedure, and so on.

Clinics often specialise in a particular area or treatment, which can lead to better results. For instance, clinics that treat many older women may have better results with this age group than those who rarely treat anyone over 40. Convenience, approachability and efficiency are important, as you will be communicating with them and attending appointments regularly. You can tell a lot from a phone call but even more by visiting. If you will be paying for your treatment, behave like an informed and assertive consumer (rather than a patient) and take a list of all the questions that you want answered. Fertility treatment can be emotionally fraught and it is likely that you will feel quite vulnerable at times, so it is important that you feel comfortable with your clinic and the staff there. You can always ask for a second opinion or change treatment centre if things are not going well.

> *One clinic I considered told me there may be an issue with treating a single woman due to the religious beliefs of the technicians! The clinic I chose made me feel totally accepted and very comfortable with my situation*
>
> *Anon*

Talking with other solo mums who have had fertility treatment, either in person or via online forums, is a quick way of getting unofficial information and impressions. Remember that these are personal experiences and opinions, so are not necessarily reflective of a clinic and your own experience may be very different.

Treatment abroad is also a consideration and this is covered in section 3.6 below.

**Consumer power**

If you are using the private system, either in the UK or abroad, do consider that this is a commercial industry and you are a paying customer. For those of us who are used to seeing health as a public service this is an important shift. Private clinics will not have same pressures as the rationed, economy-driven NHS, and you should be treated as a valued customer rather than a passive patient asking for a favour. As with any profit-making industry, your money has a certain power and there is an opportunity not to be missed in influencing conventions and standards. Be open with your clinic about what you want and how you'd like it to be delivered. For example, if you want access to a greater choice of donors, or more information about the donor (e.g. reported pregnancies or family medical history), or even if you need a clinic to have more flexible opening times.

### 3.5 Choosing a donor

Donor gametes used in the UK, including those imported from abroad, have to comply with UK law which states that:

- donors agree for their identifying details to be made available to any children conceived with their gametes when they reach the age of 18
- donors can only be paid for expenses (at set rates)
- sperm from any donor can only be used to create a maximum of ten families (although there may
- be several children in each family).

The same laws do not apply to treatment overseas and the law varies by country. Any gametes that are collected and used overseas do not have to comply with UK standards, so in this situation you will need to look into exactly what tests and checks are done, and what information you will receive. Also ask if they limit the number of families each donor can help create, in total or in each country where the sperm could be used, and if and how they monitor this.

The availability of donated eggs, sperm and embryos varies across the UK. When the anonymity of donors was withdrawn in 2005, many clinics closed their sperm banks in the belief that it was unreasonable to expect anyone to donate without the guarantee of anonymity. However, some clinics have been successful at recruiting sufficient donors by meeting their needs, such as offering longer opening hours and more user-friendly environments, as well as providing support to understand the long-term implications of donating.

Some clinics offer egg-sharing programmes to women who are having treatment that involves egg collection anyway, meaning that they have steady supplies of donor eggs, while others may have no egg supplies at all. Some clinics buy supplies of gametes from other centres or have arrangements to import them from abroad, or they might have commercial links with a clinic abroad where you would go for part or all of the procedure.

*I found it all a bit surreal. I liked each of the profiles but one in particular had written a touching message to any potential child. I thought about going through the profiles with friends and family, but in the end made the decision without consulting anyone. I remember my mum remarking that intelligence was the most important factor, but personality seemed like a bigger deal to me. In the end, I picked a donor with a creative, therapeutic job. He was the only one with an ongoing pregnancy which I thought might improve my chances. And importantly, he was the only UK donor which meant it'd be easier for any potential child to track him down if they wanted to in the future.*

*Jo, Northampton*

England's National Sperm Bank, based at Birmingham Women's Hospital, was launched in 2014 to recruit more sperm donors and promote better distribution across the country. It stopped recruiting in October 2016 due to limited success. It is not clear at the time of writing if it will be reopened with better procedures, or what measures will be taken to improve recruitment.

The amount of information available to select a sperm donor is generally dependent on your clinic or sperm bank. Some clinics will make the donor selection from their stock based on your physical characteristics and basic preferences. Other clinics offer you information about a few selected donors from which to make your choice, and others offer a choice from their whole stock. Importing gametes from abroad generally involves selecting from an online 'catalogue'.

The amount of information varies and full access to the catalogue, or access to desirable extras such as photos and audio tapes may incur a charge.

Many women report that selecting a donor from a long list with a large amount of information is overwhelming. A lot of the information provided may not be of huge importance, but can get in the way and distract you. In the US, a donor's information may determine how much he gets paid, so the profile may be less reliable if he has embellished details to increase his fee. Most information on a donor profile will fit into one of four categories: physical, medical history, personality, education and achievements. Donors are also encouraged to write a 'message of goodwill' to any offspring born from their donation, which is available on request from the HFEA or may be available as part of the donor selection process. Some parents have found that this letter is really directed at them, in a way that makes it unsuitable to the child, perhaps until they are older.

Many profiles will also contain facts and figures such as blood type, cytomegalovirus (CMV) status and reported pregnancies from donated sperm. First, find out what is essential for your clinic, such as sperm motility or CMV status. (Some clinics are more relaxed about CMV status than others). If you are CMV negative, it might limit your choice of donors if you choose a clinic that won't let you use a donor who is CMV positive.

Next, consider what really matters to you, e.g. curly hair, big hands and a science degree, or laid back, slim and no history of cancer in the family. If this reduces the number to less than five, you can then consider the less important features to whittle it down to the best. Some people have compared selecting a donor to online dating, but remember that you will fall in love with your baby even if it has a different colour hair than you expected.

*I believe nurture is more important than nature for everyday life. When it comes to medical history, nature is more important. My biggest fear is that the child will inherit some unknown condition that will be difficult to treat because we (medical profession and I) won't have the cultural / historical background to give context.*

*A.H.*

Keep in mind that many couples who happily raise wonderful children knew far less about each others history than you can find in some donor profiles, and the background the donor provides is not any indication that they will actually inherit that particular trait from the gene pool.

Believing you can choose your child's features is a risk and is one of the many areas where donor conception forces us to abandon ideas of control. As soon as your child is born, they will start to become their own person and assert themselves in so many different ways, it would be a shame to be expecting certain traits to appear and be blinkered to their uniqueness. It is liberating to accept that certain things are beyond our control and to welcome a new little individual into the world and get to know each other from scratch.

*I found choosing sperm (from the USA) an overwhelming and completely bewildering process and it seemed very odd to be shopping online for something so important. I didn't have a clue how many vials I would need per cycle and was given conflicting information from the clinic. The pricing structures were incomprehensible and there were so many different types of sperm to buy that I couldn't work out what to choose or how to order. It seemed so complicated. The sperm bank offered live email chats with their staff, which were incredibly helpful. And once I understood, it was actually very simple.*

*Jo, Northampton*

Bear in mind that it is possible to be physically incompatible with certain sperm. You may find that you have repeated failures with your first choice and need to change donors. If you have agonised over your donor and then have to switch or discover that his sperm has sold out, it might be hard to choose another and not to think of it as second best.

You may also have to decide how much to order, which will depend on what treatment you are having and whether you are paying shipment costs to import from abroad. The cost of storage and shipping may differ depending on whether you leave vials at the sperm bank or have them all sent in one batch to your clinic.

For treatments with higher success rates, you may decide to order only a few vials of sperm (and there is no point in ordering multiple samples if you can only afford one cycle of treatment). Some sperm banks and clinics let you reserve sperm (for a fee) which is worth considering if your chosen donor has stopped donating or only has a few samples left, or if you want to try for a full genetic sibling in future.

No matter what choices and obstacles you face, you will find a way to make a decision and then you can get on with trying to conceive your baby.

> *I didn't give much consideration to the egg donors. I knew I had the option to refuse, but once I reached the top of the waiting list, I just felt so grateful that someone was donating eggs to me that I said yes the same day.*
> *Jo, Northampton*

There is less choice when it comes to donated eggs and embryos as donation is much more onerous and there are fewer donors. Rather than having a range to choose from it is often a case of waiting for the first suitable donor. Treatment abroad may offer more choice of egg donors, although the conditions may differ significantly.

Some clinics/countries provide more data about the donors than others, and may use very different recruitment strategies: some may specialise in recruiting migrants or students, others in egg / embryo sharing. Try to get clear information on how they recruit and what aftercare they offer, as well as the incidence of complications such as ovarian hyperstimulation syndrome (OHSS). If they think their customers care about these factors, they will make the information available, as well as improving their practice. At this stage, the importation of eggs and embryos is still rare as storage is delicate.

Types of Donor:

**Anonymous donors**

These donors have been promised that the recipients and their offspring will never be given identifying information. Use of anonymous donors is no longer allowed in the UK, but is still an option in the USA and in many other countries. It is worth noting that with the advent of widespread and easily accessible DNA testing for genealogical purposes, anonymity can no longer be guaranteed. Many donors, as well as professionals, still believe in a duty of 'confidentiality' which is in fact no longer tenable (7).

**ID release donors**

Identifying details for these donors will be released to any offspring when they reach a certain age. The use of ID release donors is now law in the UK. However, the information does not guarantee the donors can be contacted. The details may not be up to date as clinics do not routinely keep track of their ex-donors. There is no guarantee that a donor will be alive or traceable 18 years or more after they donated, though the internet is making it easier to find people. Even if they are found and contacted, they may not be willing to meet your child, so it is important to prepare them so they will not feel this is a personal rejection.

**Known donors**

A known donor could be someone whom you have known for some time, or met with the intention of using as a donor, for instance through a website such as Pride Angel. When using a known donor there are a number of legal issues to consider. To avoid problems later on, spend time making sure that you are all agreed on the terms of the arrangements. One option is to have your donor register and go through the medical system with you, which would give you, the donor and your child the protection of the law, as well as the health checks and precautions that take place routinely in fertility clinics.

**Family donors.**

A family member who donates their gametes. In the case of single women it might be a sister, cousin or niece donating her eggs. These arrangements can provide a happy solution when everyone is well prepared and supported. The law does not allow intra-family donation where the combination would not be allowed due to consanguinity. So you can use an egg from your sister and donor sperm, but not your own egg with sperm from your brother.

**Egg donors.**

In the UK, altruistic egg donors will take ovulation stimulation drugs to produce eggs purely for donation. Often the donors are women who have had successful fertility treatment themselves. Donor eggs are more widely available overseas, but in some countries, donors are paid, so they are more likely to be students or others in financial need.

**Egg-sharers.**

Some clinics will offer younger women the option of donating half of their eggs in exchange for discounted or free fertility treatment. This has been criticised as an incentive equivalent to offering payment, but it is an important source of donor eggs in Britain and the evidence so far is that both donors and recipients are happy with the process. Obviously there is no guarantee that the donor will achieve a successful pregnancy, which could be difficult if contacted by any child conceived by the recipient in future.

**Donor Embryos.**

Donated embryos have usually been frozen after multiple embryos were produced in one cycle of treatment. Later, when the person / couple decides they don't want to use them to increase their own family, they can opt to donate them. In this situation, a resulting child would have full genetic siblings growing up in another family. In some clinics overseas, embryos may be created with freshly donated eggs and sperm that are then frozen and stored, either on order for a specific patient or in readiness for a customer in future. This tends to be more successful that fertilizing thawed out eggs and sperm. The difference would be that there probably won't be another family with genetically identical children, as there would if they were from a batch created for and used by another woman / couple. Whatever the case, it is important to clarify the exact situation.

**Altruistic donors**.

This term encompasses many of the donors above and refers to donors who do not get paid over and above the expenses that donation incurs. In the UK, donors only receive payment for their expenses, with a set maximum, so all donors are technically altruistic.

**Importing gametes.**

Due to the poor recruitment of UK donors, there is a large sperm import business and most imported sperm comes from the USA or Denmark. You can search online and choose a donor, or your clinic may have established links with foreign sperm banks to import sperm. Licenses to import sperm will only be issued if the sperm meets UK law (see above).

These donors will be registered with the HFEA and they will have had to donate under conditions that meet UK regulations. Any offspring will then have the same rights as if the donor were based in the UK. The law does not oblige donors to keep the HFEA register updated, so there is no guarantee that they will be traceable, although their name, date of birth and address at the time of donation will be made available.

> *I chose sperm from the US and had my first treatment there, then I imported from the same donor and continued treatment in the UK, not on the NHS.*
>
> *Anon*

Some overseas sperm banks will deliver to your home for self-insemination, and it is possible to get around the UK donation laws by doing this. This is not explicitly banned, but it is outside the law, and not protected in any way. It means that no UK clinic could be involved if you needed any tests or treatment, as their license would be at risk. You and your child would have none of the rights or protection UK law offers regarding health checks and quality of sperm / storage, and no recourse if things go wrong, for instance with the packaging or delivery, or the quality of the sperm when it's received.

**3.6 Treatment options**

Most clinics offer a choice of services which can be ranked in order of complexity, with the simplest unmedicated donor insemination (DI) or IUI at one extreme, and high dose medicated IVF with ICSI, and egg donation, egg sharing or embryo donation at the other.

Types of treatment are:

**DI (donor insemination)**
Donated sperm is inserted into the vagina to make its own way through the cervix and uterus to the egg. This is rarely offered by clinics nowadays and is usually carried out as home insemination.

**IUI (intrauterine insemination)**
A catheter is used to insert sperm into the uterus to find its way to the egg. This treatment is carried out in a clinic and can be a good starting point for single women with no fertility problems. While the success rates are lower than IVF, the treatment is much less invasive. In its simplest form, a woman tracks her cycle using ovulation prediction kits (OPKs) and calls the clinic when she gets a surge. She then goes in for IUI within 36 hours, to coincide with release of her egg. IUI can be stimulated, tracked and / or triggered, meaning that an ovulation stimulation drug, such as Clomid, may be used, treatment may be tracked with scans to monitor the developing follicle(s), and a 'trigger' shot of human chorionic gonadotrophin (HCG) may be used to time ovulation, and therefore insemination, accurately. Women will also need to monitor for ovulation using OPKs.

**IVF (in vitro fertilisation)**
Following hormone stimulation and scans to track follicle development, eggs are extracted, under sedation, via a needle. Eggs are then mixed with sperm to fertilise, and their growth monitored for up to five

days before an embryo or embryos are transferred back to the uterus using a catheter.

**ICSI (intracytoplasmic sperm injection)**
A single sperm is injected into an extracted egg as part of IVF treatment. This treatment is used to overcome sperm with poor motility or older eggs with harder-to-penetrate shells.

**FET (frozen embryo transfer)**
Embryos created through IVF are frozen, either because there are too many to transfer at one time, or because the womb environment isn't optimal for transfer (possibly due to risk of OHSS). The embryos are then defrosted for transfer in a later cycle. Recent research has indicated that FET may have higher success rates than fresh transfers as the drugs used

to stimulate ovulation will have had time to leave the woman's body before the embryo is transferred (8). Research has also shown that this reduces some of the risks (low birth weight etc.) associated with traditional IVF pregnancies. A woman who is planning to use her own frozen embryo or a donated embryo will usually prepare by taking drugs first to suppress her own ovulation, and then progesterone to prepare her womb for implantation.

**Double donation**
IVF can be carried out with donor eggs as well as sperm, following the same process above, but without the egg donor being treated to stimulate the production of eggs for collection.

**Embryo donation**
Embryo donation involves a donated embryo being

transferred (as with FET) at the right time in the cycle.

Although IVF has higher success rates than standard IUI, it is a more invasive treatment and there can be greater risk to the success of the pregnancy and the health of the baby. Stimulated IUI has greater success rates than unstimulated, but also comes with the risk of OHSS and multiple embryos, so you need to find a balance that works for you. Many clinics will only offer some of these options, but you should be allowed to choose to start at a moderate level of intervention before upping the stakes if you don't succeed, or to go straight to the top level if that's what you prefer. The type of treatment you choose will also influence how much sperm you should consider ordering.

Some women decide on clear limits regarding treatment: they will have a certain number of attempts with one method before they try another, and they will then have a certain number of attempts at that. You may feel strongly about this, but as you progress, your limits might turn out to be more flexible than you predicted. Even if you prefer to make you decisions as you go along, it will help to think in advance about your options and alternatives: if basic IUI doesn't work, would you consider medicated IUI or would you rather consider IVF? What are your feelings about using donor eggs or embryos if necessary?

Some clinics only offer a restricted range of services and may tell you that other options are not suitable, or not available. Alternatively they may refer you to a sister facility abroad. Always consider such treatment recommendations with due care and caution, remembering that the fertility business is a commercial industry unlike the NHS.

The clinic staff should be willing to discuss all the options so you can make an informed choice. It is HFEA policy for clinics to offer each patient a costed treatment plan, but it is important to check whether the price given covers the cost of medication, tests, counselling and other elements.

> *When my first clinic advised me to move to IVF, I asked about short protocol and Mild IVF as I had huge concerns about the impact of the down regulation process (that stops natural ovulation). I was told that Mild IVF wouldn't work for me and that I had to do conventional IVF. When I moved clinics I was recommended Mild IVF and it worked time!*
>
> *Anon.*

### 3.7 Using informal systems

Over the years, there has been a variety of informal systems to match potential donors with women hoping to start a family. These have included gay newspapers, and websites and informal 'word of mouth' networks, which are now often online too (9). The gay media advertises many services for lesbian couples that are also available to single women. Alternatively, you can put the word around and find a donor through or among your friends.

Informal systems range from a friend donating sperm 'naturally', through intercourse, or in a pot for you to self-inseminate, or via a clinic, to finding a 'known' donor or co-parent online to donate in a similar way. Informal systems can offer many advantages, the main one being cost, but they need to be used with caution to avoid some serious pitfalls as outlined below.

**Health**

It is advisable that the donor has full (general, sexual and fertility) health checks and provides a detailed medical history, including the health of his immediate family, both for your own protection and that of your child in the future. The area of mental health is critical, but more difficult to establish, since it is so stigmatised and often undiagnosed, but it's likely to have a significant genetic impact. Details about the donor's family history of mental health issues may come out in casual conversation.

**Legal**

Unless carried out through a clinic, informal treatment will not offer you, your child or the donor any of the protection that the formal system can. At best, a contract that you make would only be seen by a court as a statement of intent, which would only be upheld if it was in the child's best interests. The courts take the view that the child's welfare is paramount, that a child has a right of access to both parents, and that nobody is entitled to sign away their children's rights. The donor can claim paternity and / or access rights irrespective of any agreement you may have made or legal contracts you have put in place.

Being left off the birth certificate is no protection: many women have fought distressing and expensive court battles trying to manage informal agreements that went wrong. Having known the donor for years is no guarantee, for instance, that a future partner won't upset the balance, or the donor's own parents decide they want access to their biological grandchildren.

There is expert legal advice available, at a cost, but also plenty of material to guide you in making things as safe as you can. The gay media can provide details of specialist law firms as well as exploration of the current issues and choices. Chapter 8 looks into the legal situation further, including details of some disputes and their outcomes that have reached the news.

**Financial**

A known donor could be pursued for financial support, particularly if you ever have to claim state benefits. As above, an informal donor could decide to sue you for access to your child which would entail huge legal expenses to defend your case. If the donor's name is in any way associated with the child or if a DNA test proves paternity, he will be seen as having parental rights and responsibilities. If you use a clinic and there is documentary evidence that he is merely a donor, this will safeguard you both. If you have not used a clinic, you will have to convince the authorities that you do not know his name or any identifying details, and it would be your word against his, but DNA testing would settle the issue.

**Trust**

Informal arrangements can lead to a need for secrecy that may put you in the uncomfortable position of having to conceal information from your child, with the consequent risk to your relationship and trust. For instance if the donor is in the same community and doesn't want anyone to know, or if other recipients have asked for secrecy for their children's sake.

There is strong evidence that family secrets have a way of making their presence felt in a negative way (10): adopted children who were not told often report always having known something was amiss, even if it was only the sense that a parent was not as warm as they might have been due to having to conceal the secret. There is also evidence that secrets tend to come out in the open at a time of crisis, exacerbating the difficult consequences. And if you've ever mentioned the arrangements to anybody else, you must accept that they might be disclosed at some future time, accidentally or otherwise. Consider the risk of serious damage to your relationship with your child: could you minimise this by choosing circumstances about which you can be more open?

*I could only be treated privately and then it turned out a lack of sperm donors meant I couldn't even be treated privately so I had to make the VERY difficult decision to make my own arrangements.*

*Anon..*

Arrangements outside the clinical system can be positive and successful for all involved, and I know of many such examples. If you are considering this option, I would urge great caution and good preparation to ensure that both you and the donor have considered ALL the eventualities you can imagine. Take plenty of time and pay attention to your gut feelings, and never forget that things can change radically when an actual baby comes into the picture. Keep in mind that even married couples, who presumably know each other well and love, trust and respect each other, end up in bitter and damaging disputes. The ramifications for the children cannot be overestimated.

At all stages, try to imagine how your arrangements might look to your child: how will you explain the choices you made, and how you prioritised your child's needs? It might be easier to do this if you talk it through with someone else who can give objective feedback.

**Notes on preparing with a known donor**

If you decide to use a known donor, a good way to start might be to list the areas where difficulties can arise and discuss each of them in turn. After each discussion, you and the potential donor could record separately what you understand has been agreed and then share these notes to make sure you haven't left with different views of your common ground. Keep all notes so that you can refer back later on.

It might be a good idea to find a third person to check the progress and point out things you may not have thought of, questions to explore, points to be made more precise.

Think about the role of other people in his family: has he a partner, parents, siblings? Has he told them what he's considering doing? Will they want or expect to play a role in any resulting child's life? Even if he doesn't have a partner, it's imperative to think ahead to the role a future partner might play. You also need to consider what might happen if you find a partner later on.

A future partner might be happy to accept the situation as it is, but they might not want any involvement, might want more involvement, or might not want the donor to continue being involved. Even though you can't know, it's important to think ahead so that you can consider how you would each deal with various scenarios. Make sure you record your wishes and intentions. It might be easy for you to know you would simply back away from a potential partner who didn't accept the situation, but is the donor prepared to do the same if a prospective partner did not approve or accept the terms?

Discuss other possibilities such as one of you moving far away or abroad for work, or having a baby with additional needs who may need long term care. Talk about the level of input he expects to have on medical care, or on parenting methods in general.

If you both agree that the donor will not be involved in your child's life, you need to establish what details he's happy for the child to know and when. Consider the minimum information that a child conceived in a fertility clinic would receive, and whether you can ensure this for your child. This might include a 'pen portrait' and a message for the child, as well as a medical history covering at least two generations. Give thought to the prospect that if your child knows that you used a known donor, they may ask directly for the donor's name and reason why he's not involved in their life. How would you feel about having to deny your child information which is essentially about them?

Think about the steps you can take to protect your child, your donor and yourself in the future. Some people have used a 'memory box' in which the donor Think about the steps you could take to protect your child, yourself and the donor in the future. Some people have used a 'memory box' in which the donor leaves a message and information for the child – photos or anything that might satisfy their need for information, without actually identifying or meeting the donor.

You will never be able to cover all potential outcomes or areas of conflict, nor will you be able to predict exactly how you would feel if any of these things should happen, but at least you will have considered it and it will be much easier to discuss and negotiate when you've shared your thoughts from the start.

> *I've been considering this for two years and still haven't made up my mind!*
> *Things that have helped:*
> - *DCN Preparing for Parenthood workshop / day*
> - *Mikki Morrisette's book and Jane Mattes' books*
> - *Choice Moms mailing list*
> - *Friends*
>
> Things that hindered me:
> - *Difficulty finding other people who've used a known donor*
> - *Difficulty in working out how I'd make contact with and negotiate with a known donor*
>
> *Anon*

If you plan to co-parent with your donor (or someone else), it's worth checking Pink Parenting magazine, and the Pride Angel and Stonewall (11, 12, 13) websites for expert guidance.

### 3.8 Travelling abroad for treatment

You might consider going abroad, either because the supply of gametes in your local clinic is poor or the waiting list is long, or because the choices seem preferable.

Overall, the reports from those who've had treatment abroad are positive, but it's important to do your research thoroughly and compare different places so that you can make an informed choice. There is no regulatory body that can give information about the standards and success rates in all overseas clinics, although some countries have their own regulatory bodies.

> *I decided on double donation IVF at a Spanish clinic because it was the most sensible option for me, given my limited time and finances. I really struggled with that choice because the anonymity was a huge issue for me. It took me a long, long time to decide to go to Spain, many tears and lots of sleepless nights.*
>
> *I was in a real turmoil and I didn't know what to do. I felt immense guilt at creating a child who would never have any chance of knowing who their donors were, or even being able to present them with a picture and explanation of why I chose the donors. I spent a long time discussing it with my counsellor which gave me some perspective.*
>
> *I came to realise that just because a child has the option to trace their donor parents, it doesn't mean that they will be able to, or that if they manage to, the donors will want to have anything to do with them. And who knows, my child may never be interested in their donors.*
>
> *Jo*

You may find that local laws elsewhere are more or less restrictive than the UK. If this impacts your treatment, let them know how UK laws changed because of patient pressure to withdraw anonymity and suggest that they could lead the way in their own country. This may not help for your treatment, but could lead to more options for those seeking treatment in future.

Some clinics have centres abroad and can arrange for you to travel there for your treatment, offering the preparatory tests and treatment before you go, and supervising you on your return, minimising the length of time you need to stay abroad. This can also help to provide some continuity and perhaps some accountability.

Do make it clear if you'd like to know as much as you can about the donor, or if you would have preferred an identity release donor, or to be in touch with families who used the same donor. When they've heard it enough times, the financial incentive might outweigh the resistance to change. They will be more open to trying to change local practice if it wins customers.

### 3.9 Double donation and embryo donation: the added genetic element

For various reasons, such as age or early menopause, single women may have to consider double or embryo donation. Double donation refers to sperm and eggs that are donated separately and fertilised specifically for you, whereas a donated embryo will usually have been created for another user, and donated when the woman or couple decide not to use it. The egg may be the woman's or donated. In some cases, but generally not in the UK or the USA, eggs and sperm donated separately are fertilised and stored for donation. This is problematic because it could be considered to be 'baby farming'.

For single women, needing donated eggs can raise the complexity of donor conception to a different level as it means that all of their child's genetic background will be from donors. The hurdle of using donor eggs often seems greater when explaining a child's origins. In the early stages many feel more able to deal with the sperm donation and simply leave the egg out. This omission can make things hard later as the mother then faces the problem of how to introduce it without conveying a negative message. Telling and talking about a child's origins is thoroughly discussed in Chapter 6.

*I decided I wanted to start a family in 2006. I tried the conventional route of finding a life partner but the right man and I didn't find each other (yet!) and I decided that since my body's biology would not allow more delay and since I definitely wanted to be a mother, I would proceed solo. I made the final decision at the end of 2009.*

*After trying IUI and IVF and seeing my hormone counts go in unfavourable directions, I decided for reasons of biology, finance, a disinclination to gamble further with such heavy odds, and an undiminished desire to be a mother and to bear a child, to opt for double donation.*

*Anon.*

We all need to welcome the differences our children may display, to ensure they know they are loved and accepted for who they are. Unlike more conventional families, our children are not an expression of our relationship to a partner; we don't need to find the resemblance to him / her or to in-laws with whom we need to consolidate our links. Instead, we must make sure they know we love their individuality and the difference they have brought to our lives. Anja Karnein (14) convincingly explains that it is not the fact that we look like our parents that gives us the sense of belonging to them, but the way they respond to us and confirm our identity.

If you feel that the fact of egg donation makes this harder, take some extra time to look at the roots and implications of this feeling, maybe book extra time with the clinic counsellor. You owe it to yourself and your children to build up your confidence and self-respect. Doubts and uncertainty are not a problem in themselves, but you need to have considered them and be able to face them, to be sure they will not undermine you in raising a loved and confident child.

*I came to terms with using donor sperm quite easily because I'm a single woman. However being faced with needing donor eggs as well has been hard. "Aw, she has your nose" and similar comments are so typical when people see a newborn and I found it hard to accept that a child of mine would never have any physical characteristics from me or any other member of my family.*
*To help I read a lot about epigenetics and talked to parents of double donor and adopted children, looking for reassurance that nurture shapes a child as much as nature.*

*Kirsty*

Even when they have known about their origins from very young, children will only understand the 'missing genetic link' much later when they begin to understand the science, and may wonder about the lack of a 'blood connection'. In the throes of adolescence, this may become a weapon, as might any feature of your relationship. You need to be prepared for this and not take it personally but recognise it for what it is: a natural, if painful, part of the process of growing up and separating from you.

### 3.10 Miscarriage

Although it is widely believed that the rate of natural miscarriages is around one in three pregnancies, many of these take place so early that they go unnoticed and are mistaken for a late or heavy period. However, going through assisted conception means that you become much more aware of your body, your cycle and the smallest changes.

> *I don't yet consider my treatment a success; I'm pregnant but have had two prior losses. When the babies are born, THEN it's a success.*
>
> *Anon.*

The limbo of the 'two week wait' (2WW) is often the hardest part of the treatment roller coaster as there's nothing you can do but wait to find out if it's worked. Your period being even a few days late may be confirmed as an early miscarriage, and an early positive pregnancy test may turn out to be a chemical pregnancy. In the few days you hoped or believed that you were pregnant, you may have worked out your due date and fantasised extensively about the future. The loss of this dream can be as devastating as the physical loss. Due to the high occurrence of early miscarriage, the medical profession can be shockingly casual about them and rarely pay much attention unless they become recurrent. Even after every possible test, many miscarriages remain unexplained.

Recurrent miscarriages are so common that many hospitals have a specialist Early Pregnancy Clinic, to which you can usually be referred after three miscarriages. Research shows that the incidence of miscarriage decreases with the proximity and frequency of care and support, so they encourage you to come in or contact them as often as you need for reassurance.

It is easy to feel there is a conspiracy of silence around miscarriage. Like labour and childbirth, it is a difficult and painful event, usually part of a bigger, wonderful and positive process and therefore often pushed away into a dark corner, never forgotten but largely unmentioned. However, if you start talking about it, many women will tell you of their own experiences.

*I had two miscarriages... the first, after a year and a half of treatment, was devastating. In the ten weeks I was pregnant, I had imagined my whole lifetime, the pregnancy and the birth of my baby and onwards... so when it ended and my dreams went out the window, I was in pieces. They told me I should give my body a break and wait three months to recover. Within a short time, I had bounced back and was seeing it as a good sign, at least I knew my body could get pregnant, and I could not bear to delay trying again, so I only waited one cycle.*

*Ellie, mum to Tom, London*

Miscarriages are often sudden, unexpected, and in the early stages of pregnancy, possibly before you have started telling people and preparing your support systems. If you need emergency admission to hospital, it will be easier to call someone to bring you some nightwear and clean underwear if you do not have to explain the whole story, so consider building your support network from the very early stages.

Late miscarriages and stillbirths are even harder as you may feel even nearer to success once you have passed the twelve-week danger zone. Some hospitals are much better than others at supporting women in these difficult circumstances, for instance by separating you from women who are having other gynaecological issues and recognising the grief and trauma especially involved when a pregnancy may have been so long awaited. Some hospitals will provide special care if it is too late to terminate the pregnancy surgically, and some will acknowledge the need for special rituals such as photos or a funeral service. Some hospital chaplaincy teams provide a specialist service for pregnancy loss, often offering a non-denominational or humanist service.

### 3.11 When things do not work out

For a significant number of us, things will not run as smoothly as we hope. Many women experience multiple failed cycle of treatment, miscarriages, stillbirths and children born with disabilities. Most of us start out confident that we will succeed now that we've made such a momentous decision, but there are some things worth considering relating to the risk of having a disabled child. Appendix 2 includes practical advice from the mum of a child with life-long complex disabilities.

As with treatment options, some women also set clear limits regarding when to stop trying to get pregnant. They might decide that if treatment hasn't been successful by such and such a date or birthday, they will stop and move on. Others take a more flexible approach, and months or years later can still be struggling with the question of how much is enough.

Whether your treatment is not successful first time, you reach the limit you'd set yourself, or you find treatment, you may eventually have to sit back and review your decision. Money may determine that you simply cannot afford further treatment, or you may reach the end of your energy and hope, and need to stop to prevent further distress. Some women will give up after one or two attempts, either because that is all their budget will allow, or because they cannot face the emotional upheaval, or because they realise this is just not for them – it's too weird or too clinical.

A significant number (not recorded anywhere, as far as I can find out) will make repeated attempts over several years before getting to this point. For many women, it is simply unthinkable that they won't succeed. It's important to be aware of this risk so that you can make a more realistic evaluation at every stage and not end up penniless and bereft, feeling you have been misled and duped. I suspect that it's easier to re-evaluate and recover if you feel you've been in control and managing the situation than if you feel cheated.

Women who have decided to have a baby alone have often already let go of one dream of family life. Once this hurdle has been overcome you may have mapped out the years ahead for you and your baby, and abandoning this vision can be painful and distressing.

When people talked about 'coming to terms with your loss', I used to protest that I had not actually ever had a baby or a family to lose, but I've realised that the loss of hopes and dreams is just as painful as the loss of something that had more substance. It is important to give yourself time when you are re-adjusting your view of your future, to make sure sadness and regret don't get in the way and you can move on with clear sight and fresh energy.

We tend to feel that we must be somehow be at fault if we can't do something as natural as getting pregnant. It's so unfair that after years of striving to avoid unwanted pregnancy, it can be so difficult to succeed when we're finally ready to go ahead. Although advances in science mean that many fertility problems can be overcome, and there are many things we can do to give ourselves the best chance of success, there are still things that are beyond our control and guilt or blame are beside the point when things don't go to plan. Health writers often focus on our individual responsibility for our health, when in fact, no amount of care and precaution can ensure freedom from illness.

There is a big silence around the number of women who start trying to conceive with the help of assisted reproductive technology and have to give up. This may be because they don't want to make a big fuss; it is often the end of their hopes and dreams, and they'd prefer to mourn quietly. Another element is the fertility industry's reluctance to be open about its limitations and not wanting to discourage the customers – it's not the greatest way to promote one's business to admit how many customers make substantial emotional and financial commitment but leave with nothing.

Even if you decide to stop fertility treatment, you don't have to abandon all hope of caring for a child. Adoption or fostering may provide a solution. For some single women, these will have been a first choice, but others may feel they had to try to conceive and give birth before being ready to consider these alternatives. This is a natural sequence, it does not make these options 'second best'. If you have reached this point then the option you choose becomes the best option. It's important to feel positive, for your own confidence and for later on when explaining to your child, and if a teenager tries to use it against you in an argument.

> *I went through 11 cycles of treatment over several years but never got pregnant.*
> *One of my biggest struggles was knowing when to stop and what to do next. (I must add the story had a happy ending for me as I went on to adopt my little boy who came home just over a year ago.)*
>
> *Anon.*

Ultimately, even if you never have your own child, that need not mean you cannot have fulfilling relationships with children, be they nieces and nephews, neighbours and friends, or children in need of fostering or babysitting, tutoring, play or mentoring, or whatever you have to offer.

If being with children is just too painful a reminder of your lost hopes, you may need to re-evaluate aspects your life and make major changes to give yourself a new focus. This could involve finding work that is more satisfying or starting a project that brings you personal fulfilment. Although the pain may never disappear, you can survive the unhappiness: you have been through a lot and can use the same strength and determination to find a life worth living.

## References


1. www.britannica.com/science/artificial-insemination#ref1125363
2. www.cbc.ca/news/canada/ottawa/fertility-doctor-suspended-admits-to-4th-sperm-mixup-1.1398706 and https: everything.explained.today/Bertold_Wiesner/
3. Weschler, T.: Taking Charge of Your Fertility, Vermillion, 2016
4. https://www.nhs.uk/news/pregnancy-and-child/pregnancy-supplements-dont-help-just-take-vit-d-and-folic-acid/
5. www.fertilityfairness.co.uk
6. www.hfea.gov.uk/choose-a-clinic
7. Harper, J., Kennett, D. and Reisel, D.: How personal genomics spells the end of donor anonymity, BioNews, 3 May 2016
8. Fertility preservation: www.hfea.gov.uk/i-am/fertility-preservation/ www.bionews.org.uk/page_137015 20/7/2018 www.bionews.org.uk/page_137830 18/8/2018
9. www.prideangel.com/Information- Centre/ Fertility-Treatment/Home-Insemination.aspx
10. http://nuffieldbioethics.org/wp- content/ uploads/Anonymous_21.pdf
11. www.pinkparents.org.uk
12. www.stonewall.org.uk/help-advice/parenting-rights
13. www.prideangel.com
14. Karnein, A.: Parenthood: Whose Right is it Anyway? in, Richards, M., Pennings, G. and Appleby J. (eds): Reproductive Donation: Practice, Policy and Bio-ethics, Cambridge UP, 2012

# Chapter 4: Pregnancy, birth and the early days

*"Becoming a newborn mother changed my life. It humbled me, slowed me down, made me kinder, and infinitely more vulnerable to cruelty. Mothering a child is an incomparable rite of passage".*
Phyllis Chessler, 'Mother's Day' (2011).

## 4.1 Antenatal care

When you get a positive home pregnancy test result after the infamous two week wait, your first call will be to the clinic, if you used one, who may offer confirmation tests and checks. Many clinics will book in a human chorionic gonadotrophin (HCG) blood test, as standard, to confirm the home pregnancy test. HCG levels can vary widely within healthy pregnancies, but if the levels are low, the clinic may retest every day or so to check that levels are increasing as they should. Particularly high levels may indicate multiples. Some clinics also offer a heartbeat scan at six to eight weeks. Some clinics will include these tests in the cost of the treatment, but if they don't and you are VERY cool, you could save the money for something more practical later on.

Before you reach 12 weeks, you should register the pregnancy with your GP. The sooner you do this the better, to allow access to the services you will need. This will give you time to get to know the team that will be looking after you throughout your pregnancy. The first stage of the process is a 'booking in' appointment with a midwife who will take all your details and inform you of the local options for antenatal care and childbirth.

Be prepared for the questions about family history, blood groups etc., which will necessitate explaining the mode of conception to your midwife – if you haven't already, that is. Note that due to age or IVF many solo mums will be classed as 'high risk' and allocated to a consultant for additional routine appointments and scans. This categorisation may also limit your choices around birth, so check this out at an early stage so you can do your research and challenge any limitations if desired. If you want to see a midwife as well as the consultant, you might have to ask.

The options will vary according to the area, but you should be able to find women who have navigated these choices before you and are happy to share their knowledge. The National Childbirth Trust (NCT) (1) has groups in most areas and offers antenatal classes (at a cost, which may be means tested) as well as information on the local options for childbirth. It is worth talking to your healthcare provider to see if there are free antenatal classes in your area and if there is a waiting list. The NCT often have postnatal support groups and other activities such as swap shops and sales for baby things, as well as coffee mornings and so on.

### 4.2 Diagnostic tests

Something that will crop up early in your pregnancy is the question of antenatal screening and diagnostic tests. These are offered as routine checks, but it is important to explore the possible implications before you agree to the full range of tests on offer. Many women have found themselves facing dilemmas they wished they had been alerted to before they consented to the tests: some decisions are easier if you have considered them in the abstract beforehand.

Diagnostic antenatal tests can raise difficult questions about our feelings and attitudes towards people who are different from ourselves, such as through disability. You may feel it is unfair to have to consider these possibilities at such a delicate time on your route to motherhood, but if you wait until you are actually facing a complex reality, it will be much easier if you have thought about the issues in a more objective frame of mind. In fact, many tests will only give you a percentage risk factor, or a statement that our risk is what it would be for a normal xx year old. Consider your ability to handle this information: how much risk can you bear? How much uncertainty can you live with for the rest of the pregnancy? There are no simple answers, and you may find that your feelings change when faced with the reality. Being prepared will surely help – even if just to alert you to your friends and family's reactions and attitudes so you know whom to turn to.

Ask yourself how you would feel if tests or scans showed an anomaly. Some anomalies that are picked up are more serious than others, and some are life limiting. You could have to grapple with the decision of whether to continue with your pregnancy. Women who would not consider terminating a pregnancy under any circumstances may choose not to have any tests, others may decide to have every test in the book so that they can be prepared when the baby arrives.

If you have strong feelings against having a termination, would you want to know that there is a high risk of your baby having impairment, or could you enjoy your pregnancy more if you waited until the birth to get to know your baby? Given that many tests cannot provide certainty, the worry might turn out to be in vain. Furthermore, some tests currently carry a risk in themselves, of causing a miscarriage or damage to the placenta or foetus (although advances are being made to replace these with non-invasive tests). It can be a complex equation to work out alone.

> *I only had the basic tests, nothing else. I was willing to accept whoever was growing inside me and didn't want to risk 'damaging' them with certain tests.*
>
> *Sarah Hannah, London*

If you would consider ending a pregnancy that showed an anomaly, you will probably want as much information as possible to make your decision. Remember that some tests are not available until relatively late in the pregnancy, when you're much more aware of the growing baby inside you, leaving little time to consider the pros and cons of whether to continue with the pregnancy or not.

Doctors may assume that everyone wants the maximum testing and intervention that modern medicine can offer, so you may need to be assertive and ask for extra time, to slow the process down to give yourself time to think. You could ask for an extra appointment, perhaps with a midwife who may have more time than the doctor, to discuss the pros and cons of each test that is offered.

There is a new safer class of Non-Invasive Prenatal Tests (NIPTs) which check for Down syndrome (DS) and a few others conditions by testing the traces of foetal DNA in a sample of the mother's blood taken at

10 wks. Although many have praised the development of these tests, as a society we have to ask whether we actually feel that a life with DS is not worth living and should be prevented? People with DS and their families are protesting that if NIPTs become routine it will exacerbate the stigma for those who do have this condition, the majority of whom live happy and worthwhile lives.

If you decide to have any test that is risky or new, consider asking for a referral to a clinic where they have more experience, as they are likely to have more expertise. Clinics where they are doing a clinical trial may offer you tests that are otherwise only available privately, especially if they want to boost their numbers to complete a study.

Antenatal Results and Choices (ARC) is an excellent organisation that can help you with these deliberations (2). Remember that even with all the testing and antenatal care and precautions in the world, there are no guarantees that your child will be born in 'perfect' health, and you need to prepare for all eventualities. Many impairments happen during childbirth and no test can predict or prevent them.

### 4.3 Records and confidentiality

In principle, the mode of conception will be part of *your* medical records but not your baby's, which only start at birth. You can check with your health care provider if you have any questions about what has been recorded and even ask to see the relevant paperwork if you wish.

Registering the birth and birth certificates and other formalities:

In the UK, you have six weeks to register a birth. This will involve a trip to the Registry Office to be issued with your baby's birth certificate. A name can only go into the column for the second parent's details if they are present and consenting, or if you show a marriage or civil partnership certificate. If you are married or in a civil partnership, the certificate will be enough for the registrar to enter your spouse's name as second parent, but if you are separated check the legal consequences before you do this.

The normal procedure otherwise is for the registrar to simply put a line in the column for details of the second parent. Remember that this document will be required at various intervals throughout your child's life, and much as you choose to be open and proud about your child's origins, they may not appreciate having to share the finer details with strangers / officials in the future.

There is a campaign to have birth certificates indicate that 'additional information' is available. This information would only be available to the person named on the certificate, and would ensure that the individual has access to that information (which could be about biological parenthood, adoption or a change in gender identity) but without the details being disclosed in situations where the birth certificate is required, such as when applying for a job. This would make birth certificates a document about legal parentage rather than biological, but the biological truth would not be concealed from the child.

There are various other formalities to complete in the early days: letting your employer know, applying for various benefits, and letting your treatment centre know so they can register the birth with the HFEA. For some of these, it may help to have a letter from your treatment centre to confirm there is no named father. For full and up-to-date information, consult Gingerbread (3) or your local Citizens Advice.

## 4.4 Building networks for the future

> *I am trying to build up support networks well in advance. I have started a single women's group in the area, as there wasn't one. Sometimes if you want something done or changing then do it yourself – probably the main advice I would give! Put a post in the local shop or on your local Facebook, Gumtree or Next Door page. I got loads of response on the Facebook page for my area. It also usually tells you of local things going on.*
>
> *Lulu*

Once you are pregnant, it becomes easier to start connecting with other women whose babies are due around the same time as yours, with a view to start building the support networks that will make life easier for you and your child in the long term. For some of the women you meet it might not be the first baby, so they may have useful local experience and knowledge to share. Others will be expecting their first baby and may share the same anticipation and worries. It's a great time to get chatting informally – in the clinic waiting room, the queue for the checkout when buying baby gear, or wherever you can reasonably expect the woman standing next to you is also pregnant.

Swimming, yoga and other specialist pregnancy classes are great places to meet other women, and antenatal classes, which usually start in the third trimester, will generally be local and all the other women will be expecting around the same time. If you are worried about being the only single woman in the class, be reassured: many male partners never attend, and they will be very welcoming if you want to bring someone along - birth partner, friend or relative.

> *My biggest support network came from the new friends I met when I took the NCT course – we were all due at the same time. They have been an amazing support over the years and we have developed great friendships (us and the children). Local support is crucial and it surprised me that I have needed this just as much or even more than the friends and family I had anticipated getting support from.*
>
> *Blessed mum of two*

It's reasonable to expect that most of the women will be part of a couple, but you will soon find out if there isn't a partner, in which case you can acknowledge you're in the same boat. Regardless of their relationship status, if things start to click you can arrange to keep in touch. Some of these relationships may develop into the long-term mutual support that can make the crucial difference between lone- parenting and solo-mothering. Some of the women you meet may be in same-sex relationships, meaning that you could find common ground regarding your children being donor-conceived as well as not having dads.

This period is important for you to start making connections in your locality which will be crucial in the future. This might be a new thing for you, but try to keep an open mind: your life is about to change, and the people you want around you will also change. Other expectant first-time mums will also be looking for new sources of support and companionship, and with any luck some of them will be compatible enough to become long-term friends.

> *Preparing support networks before the baby's due – go to local antenatal classes. Look for NCT groups. I went to a place nearby called the Pregnancy and Parents Centre. It was a wonderful resource where I made lots of friends that I still see, only now it is at the school gates.*
>
> *C.A.*

However unfamiliar and daunting this appears, consider how much more difficult it will be once you have your baby in your arms. Although that in itself will open doors and attract people to you, the sleeplessness and protectiveness that come with the baby will make it more difficult to do, just when you most need the unquestioning support of familiar people.

## 4.5 Planning for the birth

Most women will want the support of someone with whom they can share their hopes for the ideal birth, who can advocate for them and liaise with the midwives. It is perfectly possible, perhaps even advisable, to have two (or more) people lined up in case one is unavailable, the labour long, or you wish them to both be there.

Consider choosing your birth partner(s) early. If you can choose more than one, that increases the chance that somebody will be available if the baby (most likely) does not appear on schedule. Make sure you list the name(s) of your birth partner(s) in the relevant section of your maternity notes so that they are allowed in if they do not arrive at the hospital or birthing centre with you. If possible, get them to attend an appointment or an antenatal class with you so they have an idea of what to expect.

Many women will choose someone who has given birth herself, so she has some direct experience. Talk through your birth plan and wishes with them, and make sure they have a copy, as well as placing a copy in your notes. Although some women may feel that they want to get on with it alone and not have to worry about someone else's needs or comfort while they are giving birth, a birth partner should be the opposite – they should be worrying about your needs and able to speak up and advocate for you. It is important to choose someone with whom you are comfortable and who is at ease with the role. It could make a big difference to your experience to have someone there, and whoever you ask is likely to feel honoured and proud.

If you have all the necessities identified, and everyone knows what will be expected of them, by the time you get to 36 weeks, you will have done all you can. In the unlikely event that the baby arrives earlier than this, it will help if you have started to prepare and plan so that your birth partner(s) can get to you and give you the support you need quickly.

### 4.6 Bonding

Bonding is the process of developing the intimate link between parent and child. It starts during pregnancy and continues after birth as your baby develops and you get to know each other and tune into their changing needs. It is important to remember that it is a process, not just an event. If things get in the way of bonding at any stage, such as a difficult pregnancy or birth, illness or other trauma, the lost time can be made up at a later stage. Bonding is essentially getting to know your child so that you understand how to respond: recognising the cry that means it's time for a feed, or providing affection or stimulation. Penelope Leach (4) suggests the main ingredient for bonding is enjoyment: if we are enjoying the contact with our child(ren) they will enjoy it too, so trust and confidence will develop. The bond of love and protectiveness will develop and strengthen with time.

If you are worried about bonding, remember that you can promote the process of attachment by giving yourself more time just to be with your baby: maintaining eye and skin-to-skin contact, talking, singing and responding to the baby's sounds, movements and expressions, holding... The evidence is that bonding is nothing to do with the genetic link, since adoptive parents also report the surge of love that characterises bonding, and genetically-related mothers may also report delays and difficulties in bonding. Bonding often happens a while after the birth, or develops gradually, so don't worry if it's not an instant lightning strike.

## 4.7 Postnatal depression

Giving birth is a massive physical and emotional upheaval even when the baby is planned and wanted. Your hormones will be in turmoil for weeks, yet you have to adapt to your whole life being irrevocably changed. Around three or four days after giving birth it is very common to go through a phase of feeling particularly fragile and weepy.

> *A local Breastfeeding Counsellor was very supportive…*
> *Sarah Hannah, London*

Make sure you are getting some rest and support and don't feel you must 'keep up appearances'. Put yourself and the baby first, giving you both time to get to know each other, and welcome those who can help around the house.

You will have plenty of opportunity to catch up with others and accept visitors when everything has settled down. Try also to get out, maybe into the local park where other new mums might gather, to find your feet in your new identity.

If you are feeling low, it's important to take steps quickly to prevent these feelings becoming more serious. Contact your health visitor or local Family Information Service to find out about local resources – mother and baby drop-ins or groups, services such as HomeStart and different voluntary organisations

*I used to be quite strong, I'd never even had an operation, but then they've sliced you in half and they just hand you your babies, and you just have to get on with it...it's harder than anything anyone can throw at you.*

*My birth plan was to have no intervention, no drugs, nothing and it was NOT what I wanted. There was nothing anybody could have done. I don't know if it was that, or that I did not know what to expect because of the donors, or just because it's a lot to cope with, anybody would be floored. But even in my twins group, it took a while for people to 'admit'. It took me nine weeks. I did feel something for them, but I was only going through the motions and it was awful. As soon as I admitted that, I felt better.*

*Sophie, mum to twins*

If the low feelings continue for more than two weeks, do get advice from your health visitor or GP. Postnatal Depression (PND) is a recognised illness, and the sooner you get help, the sooner you can start to recover. PND is not your fault any more than a virus or infection, and it is not a reflection of your mothering skills, although it can affect them if not treated. In some cases PND can develop up to a year after the birth, and in many cases, women neglect the symptoms for much longer, due to either fear and stigma, or ascribing their feelings to tiredness.

The evidence suggests that women who have had previous experience of depression or anxiety disorders are more susceptible to PND, but there is no firm evidence of causation. In many cases, there has been no previous mental illness and no difficulties surrounding the birth to explain the onset of depression. There is evidence that a lack of support or unsupportive relationships may contribute to the incidence of PND, so if you have prepared your support network and found ways of keeping any more difficult people at bay for a few weeks, that's the best you can do: solo mums are no more vulnerable than mums with partners. It is important not to feel you might be blamed for bringing it on yourself due to your choice to go it alone, as this might delay you asking for the help you need.

The first response from your GP will probably be to suggest talking therapies or cognitive-behavioural therapy, as many antidepressants are not advisable while breastfeeding. Your GP can refer you, but there's nothing to stop you referring yourself to private or voluntary services, especially if the waiting list for NHS services is long. Remember that the effectiveness of treatment depends to a large extent on the relationship between you and your therapist. Don't hesitate to shop around to find someone with whom you feel comfortable: most therapists will give you an initial appointment to discuss how they can help, which also gives you a chance to weigh up if they are a good fit.

Mind, the national organisation for mental health, has some very useful information on PND (5), particularly regarding breastfeeding and medication, as well as information on local support groups or services.

### 4.8 Lining your nest for the first few weeks

In the period of thinking and choosing how you are going to build your family, it is important to remember that although you are being strong and independent in making these choices, isolation can make it harder in the end. Your children will need you to have emotional support from family and friends, and they may need back-up carers in case you can't be there for some reason or another. It is important to recognise this possibility: accidents or illnesses happen outside of your control, or you could be required elsewhere, for instance by a sick parent or some other emergency. The better prepared you are with back up, the less you need to fear, and your children will benefit from this same sense of security.

*A few suggestions (...) I wish I'd known at the time!*

- *Always have a few extra essential items in the house just in case you run out in the middle of the night*
- *Lower your cleaning standards dramatically!*
- *Make several weeks' worth of healthy dinners for the freezer before the baby is born, but don't go and eat them before the baby's born, like I did!*
- *Be realistic (...) aim to do in a week what you could previously get done in a day!*
- *ASK FOR MORE HELP FROM FRIENDS AND FAMILY*

*Jacqui Edwards, DCN member,*
*in http://breastfeedingtoday-llli.org/single-mother-parenting-alone/*

Coming home with a new baby can be daunting. You will likely have been surrounded by people in the hospital, and you may not have had much chance to recover from giving birth. If you have prepared, you can focus on your baby and save yourself a lot of anxiety. Try to get your home organised well before your due date so that you will not have to move things around or risk knocking into things when you get home and are walking around with the baby in your arms. Work out where you're going to have the feeding and changing things so that they are near at hand both day and night, and make sure you have enough basics in – to meet your own needs as well as the baby's – so you don't have to rush out.

Learning to ask for the help you need

One difficult lesson for many of us solo mums is learning how to ask for help. Don't be afraid of letting people know how important their support will be to you. Tell your friend the brilliant cook how great it would be to have some of her delicious soup in the freezer for when the baby arrives and you need hearty food. Tell your friend with the estate car you look forward to having a bit of time with her (and a lift to the shops) when you are heavily pregnant or your baby is still tiny, and she does her weekly trip to the supermarket. Let your friend with older children know you think her kids would make great role models for your baby, and could maybe even babysit, if they will be old enough when you are ready.

You may need to set yourself a clear agenda to make sure you actually get some practice in before an emergency: decide on simple things you have never needed to ask for help with – shopping, cleaning, ironing, stocking up on ready-prepared meals, a lift to an appointment.

Try asking a few different people, and test out different ways of doing so:

- Give them an opportunity to offer: "I wonder how I am going to manage…"
- Let them know: "I need …"
- Spell it out: "Please could you …"

- Organise it: "I am making a list, can I put you down for..? Are there any days you are free / not free to help?"
- Ask a group of people for volunteers, taking the pressure off one person.

You may find some techniques more comfortable than others, and one may work better with one person than another, but the idea is to practice. This means that when you really do need help (e.g. the baby has a fever and you need someone to pick up some nappies from the shop, or your washing machine will take three days to fix and you've run out of clean clothes for you and baby) you know how to ask and who you can rely on.
If it is not totally against your nature, get a calendar with big spaces for every day and ask your friends and family to sign up to spread out visits. Get them to ring before they set out to check if you need anything picking up. Attach a list of the things that need doing, so they can see it and offer to help. Keep it somewhere everyone will see, like above where you make tea, by the front door, or in the loo!

Have a think about things you particularly find difficult (like getting the bins out on the right day, changing the cat litter, reaching stuff on the top shelf) and work out who you can ask to help you: your nearest friend for the bins, the pet lover for the litter tray, the tallest for the high stuff. Maybe it is formalities you find hard, and somebody can accompany you to the clinic or the Registry Office.

Preparing for confinement
Confinement is an old word for the first few weeks after the baby's birth, when both you and your newborn are most vulnerable. The old custom was that you really

should not be going out – in China, the mother is supposed to stay in bed for a month while the mother-in-law looks after her and the baby. It may seem self-indulgent and lazy to us and our western ethics, but it does make some sense, especially given the common factors of exhaustion and anxiety. The more preparation you can make, the easier it will be to take it easy and delay the day when you actually have to act like the independent, confident, competent and wise mother you hope to become.

Do as much as you can before baby arrives. Make sure your cupboards are stocked with essentials, fill your freezer with meals that can be heated easily and eaten one handed (no one usually mentions that the early evening when you're ready for tea is the time your baby will need you most – there is a reason why it's known as 'the witching hour').

Make sure the buggy, crib and any other equipment is put together, and that you know how to use the steriliser (if you plan on using bottles). Organise your space so that essentials are easy to grab, especially where you will be feeding or bathing the baby, or sleeping, so you don't need to disrupt everything to wipe a spill, get a sip of water, or change a nappy. Some people have baskets of essentials (nappies, spare clothes, muslins, snacks and drinks) in every room so they are always at hand.

The first few weeks

See if you can get someone (or a series of people) to stay for the first week or two. If you are managing fine, you can always let them know you are okay if they want to leave. You are unlikely to need active help 24 / 7, but it makes a big difference having someone near at hand as you get used to coping with a baby, even if only to admire how well your managing, bring you a drink or a snack when you're trapped by a feeding baby, answer the door or make a cake (and you will need cake!).

Having had another pair of hands to help in the early days, it can be daunting to wonder how you will cope when your helper leaves. Be reassured that by this time you should have mostly recovered from the birth and you will quickly find strategies that work for you and your baby. Us solo mums are very resourceful. After this period, try to schedule someone to ring daily so that you have an opportunity to talk things over if you're not sure about something: we often mull things over while being undecided whether to ask for help, someone ringing you will allow you to sound them out.

Collect tips on coping from everyone you know (especially other solo mums) – the same thing won't work for every baby, but many will fall asleep in the buggy or a sling, or if you are hoovering or hanging out the washing. Slings are great for using around the house for keeping your hands free, as well as out and about. Try a lullaby for feeding so they learn the association, and different ones for a nappy change, bath and bedtime, so they start to know what to expect and you develop your communication.

Firsts

You may find something comes as a surprise, for instance you're suddenly worried by stairs or drafts: these fears are real, and you need to find a way of managing them without limiting you. Facing them gradually and with support should help put them in their place better than avoiding / leaving them until later.

Think about the things that will be completely new and different: getting two of you ready to go out in the cold / wet (how to hold an umbrella and the buggy?), being in a crowded place, queuing in the supermarket, meeting someone for a coffee, getting on and off the bus. Watch others with more experience and note the different ways of doing things. Try to prepare as best you can and by planning them with someone whom you can count on to help without taking over. Plan simple treats like a walk in the sun or a cup of coffee with a friend to practice, before you go for the bigger challenges.

Outside support and emergencies

There are many services that specialise in specific areas – La Leche League have 24-hour help-lines for those having difficulty breastfeeding and Baby Cafes (often organised by the NCT) support and connect new / breastfeeding mums. Your health visitor should give you a phone number for any non-urgent concerns or queries. Should your baby require emergency care there may be a local paediatric accident and emergency (A&E) so you don't have to go to the general A&E. Make sure you have information about all the local resources from your midwife or health visitor, and keep them near at hand so you can find them easily, even in the middle of the night with the baby in one arm if necessary!

Premature babies

If your baby was born before you were ready, there will be the extra pressure of not having organised everything you would have liked beforehand, as well as the risk that you may have to spend most of your time in the Neonatal Intensive Care Unit (NICU) and not be able to bring the baby home for a while. In this case you are likely to require extra help from your loved ones, so you'll need to sound out who can do what as soon as you can. Consider delegating specific areas to individuals, such as ferrying stuff you need from home to hospital, contacting everyone to let them know what's happened / how you're doing, and ensuring you have moral support when you need it.

Ten tips to survive the first few weeks as a solo mum

1. Never forget, things will change very soon!
2. It's normal to be scared, daunted, bewildered, delighted, exhausted and ecstatic, often all at the same time.
3. There are very few rules: every baby is as different as every mum, so it's going to take a while to work out what's right for the two of you (and everyone will be trying to tell you how it ought to be).
4. You may have chosen to become a solo mum, but that doesn't mean you have to do it all alone. In fact, it's best to realise from the start that you can do it much better with all the help and support you can muster.
5. Asking for help is a sign of clear thinking and self-respect, remind yourself whenever you hesitate!
6. Lower your expectations and standards: your home won't be up to 'Ideal Home' standards for at least 18 years, so don't give yourself grief. If anyone comments, just ask when they will be free to help bring it back to acceptable standards!
7. Learn to say YES to every offer of help; make sure your friends and relations feel wanted and appreciated.
8. Learn to say NO, remind yourself that life may return to normal in 18 years, but that right now your priorities have changed.
9. Practice being proud: you deserve it.

10. Take each day as it comes: learn to love the moment, it's the greatest gift our children bring. (You can call it mindfulness if you're so inclined)

## References


1. www.nct.org.uk
2. www.arc-uk.org
3. www.gingerbread.org.uk/information
4. Leach, P.: The Essential First Year, DK, 2010
5. www.mind.org.uk/information-support/types-of-mental-health-problems/postnatal-depression.aspx#.Vk2TbHbhC00

# Chapter 5: Choosing adoption

## 5.1 Adoption legislation and history

Adoption has a long history as a formal way of enabling family life for children who are born into a family that cannot offer stable care. Adoption legislation legally assigns parenthood to the adopter(s) through a court order, thereby redefining the child's identity. It is a powerful tool that crosses the boundaries between the social and private aspects of life. The aim of the professionals involved is to achieve what is in the best interests of the child. They do not view adoption as a solution to fertility problems, but rather, as providing a suitable home and family for the children they are trying to place, and this is what prospective adopters need to demonstrate they can provide.

Over the centuries, social conditions have determined both the number of children needing adoption, and the regulation of such placements. In the days when the bloodline was felt to be the paramount determinant of identity, and family relationships were defined by property law, adoption was discouraged or banned, though many equivalent arrangements were made in private. At times, it was a vehicle for wealthier families to acquire unpaid help: to provide carers for elderly people, or help with farm or other labour. From Moses, Heathcliff, Jane Eyre and Pip in Great Expectations, adoption has been seen as a way for children to be placed in a family that should offer them a better future than that they were born with. Or as in the case of Harry Potter, a way of staying with a family after being orphaned, rather than being institutionalised at public cost.

The first UK adoption legislation was made in 1926, but there were dramatic changes later in the twentieth century. In the main, these were a result of the lessening stigma of single mothers and increasing state support to help single mothers stay together with their child. The legalisation in the UK of contraception in 1961 and of abortion in 1968 meant that far fewer babies were given up at birth, and more of the children waiting for adoption had a family history of neglect or abuse. However, the most common situation for babies awaiting adoption is that older siblings have been taken into care so social services know that the baby is unlikely to stay with the birth family. This could mean that the baby will have been cared for by a foster family and had no direct experience of problems in their birth family, although the family history may give rise to concerns about the baby's developmental expectations.

Of the 1100 children on the adoption register in June 2018 (1), fewer than 100 were under one year old. The largest age group were three years of age (180), and 128 were seven or older. 757 of them were classified as white British. These figures do mask the fact that babies who are adopted are often never on the register as they are placed with foster parents or kinship carers and then adopted directly (2). The Adoption Register only includes the names of children for whom adoption has been decided to be the best solution, and who still need to be found a suitable family. Thus children are only put on the register after all reasonable attempts have been made to rehabilitate them within their birth family, but some will have spent the intervening time with the family which will eventually adopt them. They do not need to go on the register, as they are not looking for a family.

The growing awareness of the long-term effects of neglect and abuse on a child has also affected adoption. It has led to a greater readiness by the state to intervene and, take a child into care sooner rather than later. Adopters need to be ready to cope with the effects of early childhood experience, family history and separation, which may not manifest until much later. However, support should be in place and training available to help adopters manage any difficulties they may encounter.

In 1975, the Children Act gave adults who had been adopted the right to obtain their original birth certificate, though birth parents can opt out of accepting any contact.

Since 2005, birth parents whose children were adopted out and have reached the age of 18 have a right to seek contact through an intermediary. The growing availability of DNA tests for genealogy searches, alongside the growth of social media, means that the age limits and restrictions on contact between birth parents and their adopted children are harder to enforce.

As the importance of sustaining some links with birth families has gained recognition, so has the practice of open adoption. This is an arrangement that maintains contact with the child's birth family. It could be anything from an annual letter and photo to actual meetings. This might not necessarily be with the parent(s) but perhaps between siblings who have been placed in separate families. In some cases, the contact may increase gradually if it is felt that the child needs to have a degree of maturity to cope with contact. These issues are explored with adopters as the placement progresses, alongside the details of talking with and telling a child about their origins. On the whole, preserving some link with the birth family is seen as a positive gesture, giving a child the message that they are accepted with all their history.

For a fuller view of the legal context of adoption, as well as guidance for those thinking of adopting, contact CoramBAAF (3). Your local authority's children and families department will have information on the local service, or will be able to direct you to the agency they have commissioned to do the work for them.

## 5.2 Why adopt?

Some single women will decide from the start that adoption is the route they want to take to create a family, but for others it is a choice that makes its way to the top of the list once other options have been considered or tried, or, occasionally, when a woman is thinking about having her second child.

Those who see it as their first choice may not feel the need to bear a child themselves, or they may have physical reasons for not doing so. Their motives are usually altruistic and they feel a sense of responsibility towards the children who are waiting for a family. Those who already have one or more children may choose to adopt because they no longer feel any urge to conceive and carry a baby again, but do want to bring another child into the family.

*...having considered the option of double donation (...) it just didn't feel right to me to go to such lengths to "create" a child who would have no genetic link to me or to anyone they would know*

*Ruth, Surrey*

Other women pursuing adoption may have had a number of unsuccessful attempts at fertility treatment, or may have had repeated miscarriages and feel they are unlikely to have a successful pregnancy. Rather than look into the use of donor eggs or other options, or if that route has also been unsuccessful, they realise that they could love and care for a child who is already in the world and in need of a home.

Some choose to adopt because they feel an older child will fit into their lifestyle better, and still others do so because they have previous experience, for instance they grew up with fostered or adopted siblings.

*I felt very ambivalent when I went for IVF and I realised I just wasn't that 'into' the whole baby thing, so adopting an older child would suit me better.*

*Sue, aged 40*

Agencies will often expect prospective adopters to wait for a prescribed period after stopping fertility treatment before embarking on the adoption process. One of the reasons is to prevent the dilemma of achieving a pregnancy and backing out of the adoption process, which could cause delay, disruption and distress for a child.

*One supervising social worker told me that if I wasn't black there would be no point in me registering; she said single adopters need to have a USP [unique selling point]'*

*Natalie, mum of one and hoping for second*

Single women (and men) may believe that they are not allowed to adopt, or that in a situation where there are not as many children waiting for adoption as there are families hoping to adopt, they will only be allowed to adopt children classified as 'hard to place' (either due to age or having additional needs).

In some cases an agency may advise that a child on their books should be placed with a single parent because their needs are such that they would fare better with the exclusive attention one parent can offer. Other agencies may take a fixed view that two parents are better equipped than one to manage a more difficult placement.

*I was told by my local authority that a newborn would be placed with a couple 'because we want them to have the best'. At the same time, they wanted me, as a single adopter with half the resources, financial and everything else, to take on a four - six year old who'd been passed from pillar to post and had attachment issues because of the way the system had mishandled their placement. As a first time parent without family support, I felt that I needed to adopt as young a child as possible to minimise the likelihood of complications in their personal history.*

*Pippa, adopter of a Chinese daughter*

If you feel that you are not receiving equal treatment or opportunities because of your situation, you might consider writing up your evidence and asking for a change of social worker on the basis that they are not a good match for you.

Although the regulations have changed around interracial adoption, some councils have less flexible policies, believing that potential identity difficulties for minority ethnic children are a non-negotiable factor. If you live in a diverse community and have friends and relations of a range of ethnicities, you might be considered more suitable to adopt a child with a different ethnicity from your own. You must be able to show how you will help your child develop their own positive ethnic identity, and how you will help them deal with prejudice and racism.

**'Hard to place' children**

It is important to recognise that many of the children waiting for adoption will be older, and/ or have additional needs that may make them 'hard to place'. Social services aim to give a birth family the chance to learn to care for their children safely and in time it may conclude that the family will simply not manage this. Time spent in an unstable environment is in itself a damaging experience, but many of the children may have been further disadvantaged from the start, e.g. by foetal alcohol syndrome or a disability.

If you think you could offer a home to a child with additional needs, discuss it with your assessing social worker as it may make the process quicker. It is important to evaluate what additional support you will need in this case, whether it is available. Bear in mind that it is impossible to know in advance exactly what the challenges you may face are. Adopters need to be prepared for whatever comes and to get suitable post adoption support, maybe for many years. Adoption of hard to place children and children with additional needs has been much studied and written about, so it is worth reading up on this area. A social worker should be able to make some reading recommendations. If you want to be considered to adopt a child with additional physical needs, your home will also need to cater for this specifically: your social worker can arrange for an assessment of the required adaptations and help you apply for grants, though this can be slow.

Older children, who have been through a number of placements, or in foster care or care homes a long time, may have issues around attachment and building relationships, or may have experienced neglect or abuse. Foster carers may become a great support in helping your child settle and bond, and a great link to the past for the child as they grow up. The evidence is that the process of bonding – building the strong and protective relationship that every child needs for healthy development – is possible in all sorts of unconventional situations. The usual conflicting pressures of adolescence, the need for security vs. the need to become independent, can exacerbate the difficulty of adolescence for adoptive children and their parents.

Just remember that no challenge is insurmountable, even if there are very difficult times. Recognising the reality and being prepared to learn and adapt with your child are the basic requirements for success. There is no science that can tell you for sure what will or won't happen, but there is plenty of experience and help out there to manage whatever circumstances arise. The only essential element is a belief in the child and yourself. That is not to say it will always be easy. Adopting is no different to birthing your child – you never know the child you are going to get, and have to be prepared to love and care for them regardless.

## 5.3 The adoption process

The adoption process is managed by local authority social services, but some authorities have contracted adoption services out to voluntary agencies. Local authorities usually provide information days and / or courses for anyone interested in adoption. These may incur a fee but are designed to ensure that people do not get into a more intrusive and expensive process without being fully informed and committed. In some areas, you may be allowed, or encouraged, to contract the assessment from an adoption agency yourself, but in all cases, the assessment will then go to an adoption panel for approval.

It is possible to be assessed in an area different from where you live, and adopters may be referred to another area to find a match in cases where it is preferable to place children further from their birth families. Although would-be adopters can only apply to one agency at a time, it is perfectly acceptable to ring several agencies to find one that feels like a good fit. Bear in mind that the assessment and training process will be simpler if it does not involve travelling long distances!

As with all prospective adopters, single applicants will be asked to demonstrate they have the personal support networks, time and financial stability to adopt. Because it has irreversible implications, the process of adoption consists of a series of stages to ensure that the welfare of all parties is fairly addressed. These can feel unduly complex or even obstructive when seen from the perspective of the adopter, but the weight of the law is on the side of the child, whose welfare must be the paramount consideration throughout the process. Many adopters go through phases of feeling that the system is against them: if you feel like this, try to remember that the social worker's priority is the child's welfare. It is important not to see it as an adversarial process, and it will be much easier if you can work with social services, even if it feels like they are working against you.

*... I had an interview with... my local authority, but got the impression that as a single person, I wasn't their ideal adopter, and that as their priority was finding two parents for the children in their care I would have to wait longer until they found a child who couldn't be placed with a couple. The voluntary agencies on the other hand were very positive about me adopting as a single parent and, as they have no children in their care, their focus is very much on finding the right child or children for the families they assess.*

*Ruth, Surrey*

Part of the adoption assessment will involve looking ahead and identifying how you might cope in different situations and whom you have around to support you and who can support your child. As with all forms of solo parenting, support will be a critical element. Although most of us will have a background of being relatively independent, it is worth preparing for the change by building elements of a supportive village around you, particularly with other adoptive families (e.g. through online groups and forums).

> *I am sure that this support network (Adopters UK Singles group) will be hugely important once a child has been placed with me.*
>
> *Ruth, Surrey*

Initial registration and checks, which will include a preparation course, are followed by an assessment and approval. The assessment is also sometimes referred to as the home study.

**The Assessment**

The assessment will look at your life history and expectations, as well as that of people who are involved with you, and will become important in any adopted child's life. Close family members and friends will also be interviewed as part of your assessment. As well as the interview, you will also have a full medical examination and smokers will be advised to stop.

> *I actually found the assessment process an enjoyable experience and learnt a lot about myself.*
>
> *Ruth, Surrey*

Many people find this experience difficult, intrusive and judgemental, but others find it positive, helping them to clarify their own feelings and hopes, and reinforcing their confidence in the choice they have made. It is essential to make every effort to establish a positive relationship with your assessing social worker, as trust is very important. Do not be afraid to admit you do not know everything; social workers are looking for adopters who are eager to learn and have the ability to reflect on their mistakes.

The social worker will write a report, which you have the right to read and comment on. However, you will not be permitted to read the reports based on your referees' interviews. If your local authority uses an adoption agency for the assessment, their social workers will have the same training as those employed by the council. One critical difference is that the agency may only do the assessments. This means that the local authority will still be responsible for placing children and following up adoptive families. An assessing social worker who works alongside those placing the children may have more knowledge of the needs of children waiting for placements, as well as more awareness of the post adoption support that's available.

> *My first social worker wasn't comfortable with me and I wasn't sure why. When talking about my relationship history, she suggested I might try dying my now silvering hair; which implied looks were paramount, and was a comment which I felt was totally inappropriate. On about her fourth visit she came out with 'Well, actually, I don't agree with inter-racial adoption.' at which point I knew her continuing my home study was pointless. I contacted the local authority, who said that the freelance social worker hadn't told them that was her point of view when they gave her the job, and I then had to wait another six months for them to find another social worker available to take my case.*
>
> *Pippa, adopter of a Chinese daughter*

Your application will go to a panel consisting of people representing adoption professionals, adoptees and adopters, as well as other relevant members of the community. The panel can accept or reject an application, or it can refer it back for further specified conditions, for example, for more information.

Once the panel has approved a prospective adopter, they can be put forward for a match with a child in the UK who needs a family. There may be variations in Scotland, Wales and Northern Ireland, so do check with your local authorities to make sure you know what to expect.

**Matching and placement**

At this stage, details of approved adopters are looked at in relation to all the children waiting for adoption in their area. The placement team social workers will be looking at strengths and weaknesses and the child's needs and disposition. Personal preferences will obviously play a role, but at every stage, it is the welfare of the child that will be paramount. The placement team will meet adopters to discuss possible matches and may share videos or photos. Following this there may be an invitation to an adoption activity day to meet children in an informal and fun environment.

If there is no suitable child in your area, there are strict time scales after which social workers should be looking further afield. Generally, if a match has not been made in six months, you should be referred on. You can play a more active role in finding a match by attending the open days that agencies and adoption teams put on, where you can find out about the children on their books, and discuss them with staff who know their background and needs.

When a match is made, there will be a series of visits, possibly including an overnight or weekend stay, culminating in the child being placed with the adoptive parent(s). This part may happen very quickly, in a couple of weeks, which can be a shock after the lengthy and time-consuming process leading up to this point.

**Fostering for adoption or concurrent planning**

In some areas, the children's services have set up a system whereby a child who is likely to need adoption but still has a chance of returning to their birth parent(s) might be placed with a prospective adopter / concurrent carer. The idea is that the carer will adopt the child if a return to the birth family is ultimately not possible, and that this will reduce the number of moves and disruption for the child.

> *Concurrent placements are still happening and some of the voluntary agencies specialise in it. I didn't go down this route as, in order to foster, you have to have a parent at home full time. As I'm on my own I wouldn't be able to afford to give up work.*
>
> *Ruth, Surrey*

There are many benefits to this process; however, the risk is that the child settles with a prospective adopter only to be returned to their birth family. For some, this possibility is unbearable, though others decide that they can take the risk, so that the child will face less upheaval.

**Legalising the adoption**

Once the child has lived with you for at least ten weeks, you can apply for a court order to make the adoption legal. In the case of an older child, or if there are specific circumstances, a court appearance might be required. An older child has the opportunity to tell the judge whatever they wish, including their wish to change their name or not. Adopted children will get a new birth certificate with the adopter's surname. Adopters are generally advised to keep a child's first name but give a new middle name if they wish.

Though infrequent, all adopters must recognise that adoptions can fall through at any point prior to being confirmed in court. This can happen right up until the last minute. The later the placement falls through, the greater the pain and disappointment for both the adopter and the child, and the greater the long-term effect on the child. Adoptions fail for many reasons, including the prospective adopter realising that they cannot go through with it.

**Post-adoption support**
Local authorities have a vested interest in supporting adopters to ensure that every placement is successful. They must provide long-term post adoption support, since problems that arise years later may originate from the adoption. This service may be contracted out to a voluntary agency whose details should be provided as a matter of course, not just when help is sought. This support should be available to adopters and adopted children separately if appropriate.

At all stages of the adoption process, it is possible you will face attitudes that feel discriminatory. Although policy states that those working in the child welfare sector should not impose discriminatory criteria, they may have deeply held beliefs about what is best for children. You can attempt to inform and educate, but do resist any tendency to take it personally. There have been cases where potential adopters have been turned down for reasons that seemed trivial, such as class, ethnicity, or minor health ailments, but these have been overturned on appeal. Be prepared to challenge any unreasonable obstacles. Adoption panels are independent and do occasionally reverse the recommendations made by the social worker.

## 5.4 Overseas adoption

Although there are many children in this country waiting for adoption, there are many more abroad. Single women may look into overseas adoption hoping it will offer greater choice, not least in the age of the child, and less waiting time. The former may not be the case, as a child may be suggested by the placement agency and you only get the option to reject. The latter is no longer true as it is quite normal for an overseas adoption to take several years, which has reduced the advantage of a child being placed at a younger age.

> *...as a single woman having tried and failed to become pregnant I chose to adopt. I also knew that having the same genes was irrelevant to me. My main wish was that I could have my children when they were as young as possible to mitigate, as far as possible, any adverse effects that their early life might have had on them. For this reason overseas adoption seemed the best route for me.*
>
> *Elaine, London*

Just as with overseas gamete donation, there can be a big discrepancy between the information provided in other countries. A further disadvantage is that you may not get to meet the current carers. The list of countries that accept single adopters changes all the time. Each country has its own regulations and processes, so the information is best researched on a case-by-case basis. It is important to get the most recent information as rules and restrictions can be imposed at short notice when there are concerns about children's human rights and the risk of child trafficking. The best resource to investigate adopting from overseas is The Centre for Adoption (IAC) (4). There is also a useful guide on the UK government website (5).

Unless you live in the country of the child's origin long enough to complete the adoption there, and obtain all the child's documents to satisfy the UK Border Agency on return, anyone hoping to adopt a child from overseas will need first to be approved for adoption in the UK.

It is sometimes possible to go to an agency in the country of choice and start the process of finding a child before being approved, but it is vital to check the legality of this beforehand. This is banned in many countries to reduce the risk of grooming or child trafficking.

Even if the overseas agency placing the child does not require it, you usually need to go through the full adoption process and get the panel's approval to bring your child home to the UK. Unless the child is adopted from a country that is approved under the Hague convention, when the adoption order from the country of origin is enough, the adoption will need to be confirmed by making a formal application for court order in the UK.

There are many ethical questions around overseas adoption as well as examples of poor practice. It is important to consider how you might discuss your choices and the child's origins with them in the future. You owe it to them to ask questions of yourself and the agencies involved to ensure you are protecting their interests as far as possible.

Local adoption agencies overseas require payment for their services, so this also puts you in a good position to promote better practice by expressing your concerns for women who are giving up babies for adoption. If adopters are asking for assurance and evidence that the birth mothers are receiving good care and support before and after the adoption takes place, the agencies involved will appreciate that their clients have a healthy concern about the welfare of the birth mothers, which should lead to them improving the care they provide. Understanding the local conditions and the reasons that the child was available for adoption, as well as taking an interest in the welfare of the birth mother, will also put you in a positive position for discussing origins and adoption with your child later on. If you can frame this into a positive picture, it will help your child develop a positive view of themselves and their origins.

If you are considering overseas adoption, it is imperative to do as much research as you can before going ahead, and to stay on top of this to make sure you are not caught short by any changes in local laws or practices. If there is any irregularity, the adoption might not be confirmed when you get back to the UK, leading to insecurity and uncertainty for your child and your family. Try to make contact with other families who have children from your country of choice so that you can benefit from their experience, and so that your children can benefit from knowing others with the same story.

### 5.5 The financial aspects of adoption

Although in principle adoption should be equally available to all, irrespective of material circumstances, financial support for prospective adopters is limited. The assessment for adopting a child in the UK is provided free, but for those planning to adopt a child from overseas there is a cost for the assessment. For overseas adoptions you will also need to pay for the child's care and health checks while they wait for placement, as well as paying an agency fee to the organisation you are working with abroad. This can add up to several thousand pounds on top of the assessment fee, the visas and the cost of travelling abroad to meet and bring home your child. The UK court fee for the adoption order of £170 (2018) is payable by all. At the time of writing, the overall cost of overseas adoption is estimated at £10,000 upwards (6).

Adopters are entitled to statutory adoption leave and pay, parallel to maternity provisions. Once you have adopted, you will be able to claim child benefit and may be eligible for income related benefits as well. You may also be entitled to an adoption allowance to help with any additional costs. Some authorities pay additional allowances to parents who adopt a child with additional needs. Those living in social housing may apply for a transfer to a bigger home to accommodate a child, or may be entitled to a grant to adapt their home accordingly. Information on grants and benefits will be available from the local authority or housing association, but may also be provided by the adoption team.

The issue of finance is one where single women can start to feel discrimination as the assumptions of the authorities are usually based on what it might be reasonable to expect of a couple. For instance, some local authorities expect an adult in the adoptive family to take a year off work to integrate the new child in the family. This might be difficult if you are self-employed or cannot cover your costs over and above the statutory 39 weeks adoption pay. Some employers offer far more than the statutory minimum, so do investigate this.

## 5.6 Long-term fostering

The option of long-term fostering is worth considering for those who want to be involved in a child's life but do not want to go through the adoption process, although it does not offer the same responsibility and security as adoption.

Advantages:

- There are many looked after children who need a long-term placement but for various reasons may not be 'freed for adoption'. For example, because they have ongoing positive relationships with the birth family, even though there is no prospect of reuniting them. Foster carers would need to be committed to supporting this relationship, but would otherwise be responsible for the child's everyday care and upbringing.
- Foster carers are paid an allowance, as well as expenses, and can claim holidays and regular respite care (where the social services department will find alternative care for the child when they need a break).
- Foster carers get basic training and ongoing support, and further / specialist training as needed.

- In addition, you might feel that looking after an older child would fit in better with your working life, or with your friends or family.

Disadvantages:

- Foster carers never have parental responsibility for the child: they must consult the social worker about all major decisions and accept the limits and standards that are set. They will have regular formal reviews as long as the placement lasts.
- The assessment process of foster carers is as thorough as for adopters, so it can be just as challenging.
- Foster placements may end abruptly and unexpectedly if the birth family's circumstances change. The child's welfare is, as always, the primary consideration, and the foster carer's feelings are simply not a factor in the decision, which can be distressing and painful.

As with adoption, there is the option of using independent fostering agencies, which provide their own social workers for assessments and long-term support. They may be less pressured than council workers, but that is not always the case. If you do not feel able to make the lifelong commitment that adoption implies but still have space in your home and your life for extra children, you might consider shorter term fostering, or fostering teenagers.

## References

1. www.adoptionmatch.org.uk/statistics/
2. https://assets.publishing.service.gov.uk/government/uploads/system/uploads/attachment_data/file/664995/SFR50_2017-Children_looked_after_in_England.pdf
3. The British Association for Adoption and Fostering (BAAF) has now been taken over by the Coram Foundation and become CoramBAAF. A good place for information, many leaflets to download. https://corambaaf.org.uk/fostering-adoption
4. The Centre for Adoption (IAC) www.icacentre.org.uk
5. www.gov.uk/child-adoption/adopting-a-child-from-overseas
6. https://holbornassets.com/much-cost-adopt-child-uk

Resources and further reading

Wise, J.: Flying Solo: A single parent's adoption story, CoramBAAF, 2007

## Chapter 6: Telling and talking

*"I don't want things harder than they are,*
*I want to protect him from the names and stones, I'd love it all to be different..."*
Jackie Kay, 1991.

*The poet Jackie Kay voices what many of us feel, but I propose that we must actively support our children to manage their differences with grace and confidence, and resist the temptation to 'let sleeping dogs lie'. The fact is that they will 'wake up', and our kids will need to have learned to respond.*

*Huge thanks to the Donor Conception Network for giving me permission to use this chapter title, which was coined for their groundbreaking books and flagship workshops. You can buy a book / book a place on workshop from the website (1). The title emphasises the fact that telling is not just an event; it is a process that continues as your child develops. This chapter will look at the specific issues for solo mums.*

### 6.1 What to say, to whom and when?

Single women often talk to family and / or friends when they are considering trying to conceive and going through the process, although some women choose not to discuss their plans with others. However, once a pregnancy is announced, or you have an unmistakable bump, you should be prepared to meet the inevitable enquiries. It is likely that everyone who knows you will have the question on their lips, whether they say it aloud or not. They may want to ask you lots of questions, but it is up to you how much you tell them.

However much (or little) you decide to share, remember that as a rule of thumb, if you present something confidently and positively you are likely to get a positive response. If you seem unsure of yourself, nervous, or fearful, people will notice that and may feel concerned about your decision and how you will cope. So, when telling people, whether about your pregnancy or how you conceived, if you show that you're excited about the news and happy to share it with them, they will be less likely to worry about you or for you.

While some women will be open about their solo parent status or their baby being donor conceived with everyone and anyone, others may be happy to let some people know, but not wish to discuss it with all and sundry. This is also fine, especially if you make sure people know that this is about you and not them. If you are clear that it just feels private, it's not that you don't trust them, it will be easier for them to accept it graciously. If you don't feel comfortable sharing any of the facts, you need to find a way of making this clear without being standoffish – maybe by being unemotionally honest and clear, for instance just stating (with a smile) that the details are private. Practice this in front of the mirror to make sure you can say it without wincing! If you look positive as well as friendly, people are more likely to respect your privacy.

Many people find donor conception fascinating, even more if you are choosing it as a single woman. No matter how much you want people to keep it to themselves, this is simply not realistic. You can make a specific request, e.g. to keep your name out of it, explaining that you are not ready to be asked about it by everyone yet. It is helpful to think about what you want to say, and how you tell people. For instance, you might want to choose the wording you use so that it's not sensationalised – refer to the clinic rather than the sperm bank, and avoid using nicknames for the donor(s). You can also tell people you are happy to discuss it further with them, or refer them to something in print (e.g. one of the DCN publications), if they want more information.

> *...say nothing you don't want to unless you're asked. And if you don't want to say anything then turn the question back on the asker in a kind, empathic way. They are obviously curious, but by showing them what it feels like to be asked something inappropriate, they usually get the message.*
>
> Helen

One of the situations which comes up for all of us at some stage is questions from doctors or others in official positions – the passport office or immigration department or the person who's interviewing you for benefits. It helps if you know why they need the information, where it will be recorded, and on whose records (yours or your child's). You can ask for the information about conception not to be recorded on your child's documents, as it's not relevant, and you can consider if you prefer 'no details available', 'father unknown' or simply a line or a blank. In some situations, you might be asked to prove that you used donor conception and that the donor's anonymity is protected, for instance when travelling/ crossing borders; this is becoming more frequent due to increasing awareness to protect against child trafficking. It's a good idea to get a formal letter from your clinic to keep along with other important documents so that you don't have to try to obtain a copy in a hurry a few years down the line, which could be difficult if the clinic has moved or closed down and nobody remembers you.

**Referring to the donor(s)**

The donor will most likely be another topic people will want to ask about. It is worth trying to think ahead, as the donor's position in the equation will change radically once your baby is born. It is important to take the long view: you are setting the foundations now for your future as a mum, and the question will come back regularly over the next sixteen years or more. In the early stages, the donor mainly figures as one of the questions you need to make decisions on – as dealt with in Chapter 2. Choosing the donor can make a great topic of conversation, if you are the sort of person who has enjoyed intimate chats about wording your lonely-hearts advert or choosing a date on a dating website. If you have treated the exercise as a bit of a game, you may need to change the tone when you are pregnant. Make sure your family, friends and acquaintances understand the limits and how they change with time; do not assume they will follow your lead without any discussion.

Most solo mums prefer to depersonalise the donor(s) when it comes to considering the child, not wanting to predetermine their role in the child's development. If you have discussed them as a matchmaking exercise in the early days, you will have to make it clear it has changed when your baby is on its way. For instance, you may prefer to allow your child to develop their own personality and traits rather than relating everything to the donor. Consider the terms you want to use.

At first, your child will learn your language without question, but when they move out into the world, they may come across different terminology and definitions, and eventually they will choose their own words to define themselves and their relationships. You can help prepare your child by discussing the words which they are learning in the context of other families around them: point out the similarities and differences. When they are older, they will choose their own words, but for now, it is your privilege to set the scene.

*I'm not sure I've found an 'easy' way [to talk about double / embryo donation] but it gets easier the more you do it. I usually reference the fact that I am an older mother (that much is usually obvious) and use the 'heroic amounts of IVF' line. If the conversation continues (and especially if they seem to assume it was purely the IVF that brought success at my age and they're thinking they might be similarly lucky) then I start with 'I needed a donor'.*

*Since I'm single the assumption is always that I'm referring to a sperm donor, but if the discussion suggests to me they are a person I am comfortable disclosing to, then I later mention that an egg donor was involved.*

*Maggie, soon to be mum of two*

Further down the line, consider how you'd like your friends to explain things to their children and how you'd like your children's friends to understand the situation. The likeliest scenario is that older children will ask questions about the 'missing parent' and not be satisfied with your child's answers – for instance saying that everyone 'must have a dad'. Many of us are wary of introducing other children to terms and concepts their parents might not have raised with them yet, and for which they might feel they are not ready. It is going to be much easier if you have discussed it with the parents before their children ask any questions, so they can intervene more consistently when you are not within reach. They may appreciate not having to work it out from scratch.

## 6.2 Family and friends

When you are thinking of starting a family, you will probably think more about your own family relationships and how they will affect you and your child. Maybe you are lucky and there are family members in a position to help or support you, emotionally as well as practically. If you have been talking to your family and friends as you make your decision, you will already know where they stand.

> *...men have reacted quite differently to women when I explain. It appears there is a sisterhood effect, women giving me encouragement. Men on the other hand are neutral at best. They just don't understand, I guess.*
>
> *Rachel*

However, if you have waited until your pregnancy is confirmed you need to face the chance that those who thought they had a close and important relationship with you may feel hurt that you did not confide in them from the start. Try to find an explanation that focuses on you rather than them, for instance that you were too frightened it would not work or wanted to wait until you were sure. Remember that it helps when you can frame the disclosure positively. You could introduce it as something exciting that you are finally free to tell them, rather than hesitantly, unsure of how they will react. With any luck, any disappointment they feel at not being the first to know will fade once you let them share in the excitement of looking forward to the baby's arrival and their positive role in your new life.

Finally, it is useful to remember that others may have experience of some of the things that you have faced or are facing but never talked about it. If you are open, you might find an important source of support that would otherwise not have been apparent. Many of us have been surprised at friends or even family divulging using fertility treatment in the past, and others saying how they wished they had had the opportunity themselves. These friends may well become those who are most ready to provide help and support in the future.

## 6.3 Workmates and acquaintances

You need to decide when and what you want your colleagues and acquaintances to know. You will be seeing workmates on a regular basis so there will be casual opportunities for the subject to come up.

You can use a 'drip-drip' technique, assuming also that there will be some sharing of the news when you are not in the room. With acquaintances you might just decide on a short statement you use when you bump into someone 'Yes, it's good news, I'm due in (month), and no, there's nobody else around, I'm going ahead on my own....'

*I arranged a meeting (...) I put the pictures from my scan down on the table. There was ten seconds of silence: half of them covered their speechless gasp and the other half shrieked with surprise and joy*

*The enquiry about the identity of the' happy father' followed naturally, and I just said we don't always need a man by our side for everything, right? They laughed (by the way, they are all women) and there were lots of hugs and kisses...*

*Those not at the meeting were more curious about the man behind this as they don't know my age, and the rumour went round that it must have happened when I was on holiday in Greece.*

*TIP: You don't have to justify everything to those who are not part of your personal life, you can let them think whatever suits their values / culture...*

*A solo mum in love with her new life and her little prince*

As with any pregnancy, there will be an impact on colleagues in terms of covering for your absence and / or welcoming a temporary replacement. Much as it should not make a difference, it might affect their reaction, as it is possible your pregnancy will be more unexpected than if you were in a relationship (if your colleagues know that information about you). Try to acknowledge their point of view and do what you can to minimise the disruption, e.g. by giving good notice of when you hope to take your maternity leave so cover can be planned.

*I had a fairly close-knit group of quite gossipy neighbours; I didn't relish the prospect of telling them. I also knew that, if I didn't proactively tell them, they might ask pointed questions.*

*Thankfully, a friend of mine who lived in the street came to my rescue by telling one or two of them that I was about to have a donor conceived child. They then told everyone else.*

*As a result, nobody asked any awkward questions and everyone's curiosity was satisfied.*

*Liz,*

**6.4 Dealing with negative reactions**

In all the years of listening to women's experiences, it is amazing how rare it is that they meet negative reactions. Maybe one factor is that we expect them and make the decision not to be put off, and then when they come they are so minor they are quickly forgotten.

Although religious fundamentalism is less common in the UK than it the US, where it's often the cause of friction between parents and their daughters who break away, it does happen, and sometimes very painfully. The bottom line is that once the decision is made and there is a child in the picture, you owe it to your children to protect them from any blanket disapproval that is nothing to do with them. If this is a risk in your family or community, you need to consider ways of moving from a situation where your child risks being victimised or stigmatised. In all close groups there will have been individuals who broke away. Find out more about them and they might lead you to a more accepting community for your child. I know of several women who have gone 'church shopping' when they want to find a more welcoming spiritual home. Start this search early, it will be easier to bring your child into a community you are already getting to know than if you start from scratch with a new baby.

### 6.5 Whose information is it anyway?

I've often heard women express doubt about telling anybody about their child's conception, on the basis that the facts 'belong' to the child and you will let them decide later on who / what to tell. Although this sounds respectful of the child's rights, it is flawed in several senses.

Firstly, there will be occasions when your child might need the adults around to explain things, particularly when they are too young to take the responsibility themselves. Older children might pick up the issue at school, at the childminders, or in the playground and ask questions beyond your child's capacity to explain, or just insist your child is either stupid or lying, because everybody has to have a dad somewhere.

Our children are entitled to the support of the adults around them, to know that they will step in with such situations. One of my son's teachers seemed embarrassed when I told her at the start of the year and told me she didn't need to know, so I explained why I thought she did, with my then eight year old by my side.

Secondly, if your child witnesses you sidestepping the questions, they may get the impression that it is something to hide. If you can model simple and honest responses, they will learn how to handle similar situations comfortably themselves. Much better to know they can give an answer that satisfies and move on than get stuck trying to explain things and feel it is too strange to be believed. It will help your child 'own' the truth.

Finally, there is a level on which it is actually your information, not your child's. In most families, the details of their conception is not a part of the children's identity, it is considered a private matter that is part of the parents' relationship and quite inappropriate to share with our children. Our children need to know why their family is the shape it is, and especially that it is NOT that way due to anything they have done, but they do not need to know the intimate details. So they need to know that the donor did this to help others, not in order to be a dad. They do not need to know about your history of failed relationships so much as they need to know that you really did want to be a mum so you chose to have a baby – the medical details are only important when they are ready and asking for them.

Note that there may be important gender differences here: I recognise that girls may have a greater interest than boys at this stage, as they are more immediately aware of their developing fertility.

**Double / embryo donation**

For single women, using donated eggs can raise the complexity to a different level. Many feel more able to discuss the sperm donation and leave the egg out of the explanation in the early stages. When they face the problem of how to introduce it later, the omission can make things harder. Try to integrate it right from the start, e.g. 'I didn't have a man to be a daddy and my eggs were not working either, so I went to the doctor, who had some sperm (kindly donated by men) and eggs (kindly donated by women) that they used to start you growing. When they knew it had worked, then they put the little embryo into my tummy to grow into a baby ready to be born.' When your child is ready, they will ask the questions to fill the gaps in their understanding.

**6.6 Talking to children**

The DCN booklets on Talking and Telling, which come in four developmental stages, give a good framework to track your child's changing perspective over the years.

The evidence from research (2) is that donor conceived adults who grew up knowing about their origins are less likely to feel resentful about it. Donor conceived adults who found out later may feel they were deceived by the people they should have been able to trust the most, and are left with a sense of losing the identity they believed was theirs. Just as with adoption, it is now the accepted standard that children should grow up knowing the facts from the earliest age, and we need to be finding age-appropriate ways of answering their questions as they grow up.

For single women raising donor-conceived children, we have to recognise that our children may meet prejudice and false assumptions about their family, origins and potential. We need to arm them against feeling constrained by the stereotypes, by openly sharing our pride and confidence in our decisions and choices and providing them with the words and concepts to use when they are questioned. Mostly this will be by other children out of sheer curiosity and not intended to be a challenge; they need to feel comfortable and familiar so they do not get defensive.

**The developmental stages (roughly) and your child's grasp of family formation:**

Babies are pre-verbal for around eighteen months, this time is very important for setting the foundations for verbal and conceptual development. Your baby will be learning how to communicate with you (and vice versa) so it's important to use every chance to build up their experience: your tone of voice and other nonverbal cues are especially important at this stage. They will be learning to follow your example – for instance, responding to your smile, relating the page and pictures to the words you're reading, building associations and developing ways of perceiving.

By the time their first words come along, they will have developed specific interests (Why was my son's first word 'scissors' when most babies were saying 'mummy' or 'milk'?). You can start linking ideas up for your baby, referring to the 'Mummy bear looking after her baby bear', 'the puppies playing nicely' and the 'Mummies / daddies taking their children home for supper / bath / bed' in books, or whatever ideas you'll want to build on in the future.

Many of us use picture books such as the DCN's Our Story books to 'practice' with our children long before they understand the words, so they and their children grow into the story together.

**Infancy**: This is the time when things start moving very fast. Most toddlers will be taking in everything around them very openly. Things that are too complex (arithmetic, genetics) they will simply ignore until they have the language and interest to ask the right questions. That does not mean that they will not notice or take it in, just that they are only ready to understand so much detail. The endless repetition of 'Why?' tells you they want to keep you engaged, but can't verbalise a more specific question.

This is when you can use every possible opportunity to talk about different family structures and relationships – the ducks on the pond, birds building nests, other families in the park. 'Look at how the mummy duck is keeping all her chicks in a line', 'Is that a daddy duck or a granddad coming to help?', 'Is that two daddies with the baby in the buggy?' and so on... At around three our children are discovering how things work for themselves, and some of this will involve testing out specific ideas – such as 'Where's my daddy?' or calling other men 'Daddy' to see what happens.

**Childhood:** Once children develop language skills, they can ask questions, to explore and discover what they want to know. Now you have to be ready to listen to the actual question, and target your answer precisely. This is when you need to think about your choice of words, as this will be the basis of how your child learns to understand their own family.

One of the problems that most of our children will meet at this stage is that they will be questioned by other children, often older, and their explanation may be out of synch with the other child's knowledge or vocabulary. When my son got fed up with kids who 'didn't get it', he would tell them to ask his mum, which sometimes worked.

Some people are hesitant to use 'technical' language, fearing that other adults may interpret that as sexualised. Remember that the link between sex and baby-making is as yet completely unknown to your child. It will not threaten their innocence to use words that are more often used when talking about adult relationships, but you may need to deal with other adults' reactions.

You need to make it clear to your children that they can ask for more detail but you also need to gauge what they want, and avoid flooding them with detail that is not relevant. For instance, they're unlikely to have any interest in the process of conception except for how the sperm got into the test tube / your tummy until they are seven or eight. It is later still that they start to wonder about the link with family relationships – for instance my son was about nine when he had to check if his donor was also in any way a father or dad.

At this stage, you can also start talking in more detail to children about origins – explaining how cousins, aunts and uncles are related and how traits are passed on through the generations by DNA – looking at how earlobes and tongue rolling are linked to our genetic background. You can start relating your child's traits to what you know about the donor and introduce the concept of half-siblings.

**Adolescence:** As they reach their teens, our children are developing their own identity and getting a sense of themselves as individuals with a life and future separate from the family. Part of this process is testing of boundaries, and they need acceptance and support just at the time they are becoming more reluctant to confide in you or accept everything you say without question. Most adolescents will on occasion behave in a manner that feels challenging and rejecting of your authority, and you need to be ready for the likelihood that they will throw aspects of your parenting back at you. You can be best prepared by considering how your relationship with your child is developing from the start, and being clear that all problems can be addressed, irrespective of the lack of a dad or partner in your family. You do not have to be all things to your child anymore, so, if you can, find other adults who can support you. Your children can develop and practice alternative relationships with different adults, the more the better, and they will have a sounding board to remind them how your being single is a strength, not a deficit.

**The importance of openness:**

If I am dogmatic about anything in this book, it is about honesty and openness. I know that it is both a critical component of trusting and respectful relationships and that it is a difficult area when we have had to resort to unconventional processes to create our families. I can see how tempting it is to play down the features we may wish were not true, but it is important to recognise our own feelings and ensure we are not passing on any conscious or unconscious guilt or shame to our children. The evidence is that secrets often assert a strong (if silent) presence in families, being experienced as coldness, fear or shame. Children may even imagine something much more terrible is being hidden from them. Secrecy is a corrosive force in family relationships.

If you feel hesitant, consider getting some help. A support group of other solo mums is probably the best place to share your feelings and get the reassurance from others who have faced the same problem. If this is not an option, a counsellor can help, but you may need to shop around to find someone that you connect with, as well as someone who has absolutely no implicit beliefs about conventional family structures. Remind yourself that every family has its weak points, and every adolescent will find them. Your teenager needs you to show your confidence and self-respect when they press your buttons, so they learn you can live with imperfection. If you hope they will become well-adjusted adults who can recognise their own strengths and weaknesses, you must be able to model this for them.

To back this up, check the research on secrecy in adoption as well as in donor conception, and what attachment theory has to say about the impact of adoption. If you read reports from adult donor conceived people, you will find many reports of the sense of deceit, distress and confusion that results when the secret is blown when they are older.

For those who are not sure about telling their children about their origins, please consider the likelihood that they will find out later. It won't be long before they can see for themselves that their family is not the typical shape; they deserve to have the words for this before it becomes an unspoken taboo. This would have a big impact on your relationship, as they will feel that you are keeping something important from them. Although you may feel that you had their best interests at heart, they are likely to feel deceived and let down by the one person they should be able to trust.

Secrets often come out in a crisis, when guards are down and feelings are high, so the disclosure could be tainted by the feelings related to a difficult situation. Many older donor conceived people who were not told from the start found out the truth during a family crisis or a row, hardly the situation for calm discussion, sympathy or re-evaluation. In other cases, it is disclosed by someone who assumes you have told them already, so if you have ever told anybody, you must recognise that it may get back to your child, and that it could happen when you are not around to deal with the fall out.

Studies of adoption show that not knowing was the main difficulty faced by adoptees. In 1972, the Houghton Report led to adoptees acquiring the legal right to their original birth certificate when they reach the age of 18, which led to disclosure becoming an expected commitment by adoptive parents. There are a number of donor-conceived adults who speak of the distress not just about having been misled, but also of being denied information which they feel is fundamentally theirs, about their genes, roots and identity. To quote Wendy Kramer's aphorism, we need to be giving our children roots to make them strong as well as wings to fly. The roots may be the certainties, such as that they are wanted and loved and central to your family, and the wings consist more of questions rather than facts. If we are as open as we can be, our kids can grow up comfortable with those questions, not feeling they are off limits.

This approach is based on a belief that it is up to us to build our children's resilience so that they can cope with reality, something which may not always be positive or simple. Attachment theory suggests that this happens through building bonds and connections with your child, and responding consistently to their needs so that they have a strong sense of self. Systemic family theory suggests we should be helping our children learn to soothe their own anxieties from the start, by using the 'systems' – the relationships, skills and behaviour patterns that are part of the family dynamics.

Either way, if we make every possible effort to show our children how to accept differences and diversity around them, so they can respond confidently to challenges, we will be building a good foundation. Whether it is their origins or their family structure, or the fact they have freckles or wear glasses or some other feature, every child will come across remarks that could hurt or upset. The child who knows that we are all unique and different, and who is comfortable with their self will be less vulnerable; the remarks are less likely to have a negative impact. When a child reacts strongly to something, it may feed into the other child's need to assert their power or superiority and the teasing turns into bullying. Younger children may be less aware of differences, but the world at large is teaching them that looks, size and conformity matter and they will use the examples that are all around to assert their own position.

**Talking about the donor:**
Solo mums have varying amounts of information about the donor, and it is not immediately obvious what status this information has in the fuller picture. I believe this is distinct from the facts around the family type and how the child was conceived. The difference between a donor and a father can get blurred, for example if you discussed choosing the donor with friends, you will

have opened the subject early on, but this was something about which I felt particularly uneasy.

I did not raise it at all until the issue became a joke among my friends, that the donor was obviously a farmer or construction worker to account for my son's obsession with heavy plant machinery. At that point, I disclosed some of the facts that I had – I would have been delighted for the donor to be a farmer, but I was secretly worried that I might find out his job was actually something with which I would have more difficulty. Eventually I wrote to the HFEA to get the fuller details, and in fact he was even closer to what I might have chosen if I had overcome my reticence and not left it to the nurse. He definitely did not have anything to do with heavy plant machinery, but neither was he an arms manufacturer or hedge fund manager.

With young children who fantasise about how life might be, it's easy enough to enter into the fantasy and enjoy it together. You can have a good time talking about 'what if the donor was x, y or z...', but it could be harder if there were real facts to fit in – e.g. he studied dentistry, so might our dentist be the donor, or know him from college? If he has brown hair, every man with brown hair becomes a candidate and so on. My main hesitation is that the donor becomes someone with a ghostly place in your lives if he gets too many attributes before your child is old enough to keep clear about the facts, i.e. that he is NOT involved in any personal way.

Explaining donor anonymity is also important, so that our children understand that it is not us barring their access to identifying information, and so that they grasp that they may be able to learn more in the future. I think it helps if they understand that at 18, they may get more information than you have been given, that they will have rights of their own and their need is recognised as separate from you. However it is important to explain that there may be nothing more than information; the donor may not actually be found, e.g. because he or she has changed name, moved abroad or has died. Even if he / she is found, they might not be interested in meeting or even knowing more about their offspring. They agreed for their details to be disclosed 18 years ago, but many things could have changed since then.

## 6.7 Children with different origins in the same family

Families can be complex, or become increasingly so as time goes on. It is possible you had a child from a previous relationship before moving on to have a donor-conceived child, or once you have a donor-conceived child you may meet a partner who has children from a previous relationship. You may also go on to have a child with a new partner. You could have children with different donors or a child through adoption. Whatever the situation, telling becomes more complex when each child has a different story, and you may worry about how to manage this information to ensure that there is no rivalry.

Although not exactly the same, there has long been a precedent in reconstituted and 'blended' families. One of the important things that has been learned is to be clear about whose worries you are feeling, and to ensure that all family members get a chance to express their own feelings. The chances are that your children have quite different points of view. You may fear one child is feeling disadvantaged due to different origins, when in fact, the grief is simply due to not being an only child any more.

As far as possible, give your children opportunities to express their own concerns and questions individually, preferably privately, and never assume you can guess! It is more a case of finding out what they want to know than of working out what to say. We are often surprised at what aspect of the information is of interest and needs clarifying. There is no point in agonising about how to explain one thing when it is something completely different that is concerning them. If you are prepared to say you do not know, you will have to find out or work it out, you can always give yourself time to answer the unexpected question.

As mentioned above, focus on ensuring your children have a positive view of diversity. This will help them be proud of their unique origins and attributes as well as seeing others as being interesting for their differences, and it will make acceptance more natural. Of course, any child in every family situation (even full siblings in a 'traditional' family set-up), needs reassurance that they are important to their parent(s), and regular one-to-one time with you can reinforce this.

**References**

1. www.dcnetwork.org
2. Kramer, W. and Cahn, N.: Nuffield report 2013 'Finding our Families', Avery, 2013

# Chapter 7: Solo mothering and beyond

*"Very little about the gender of the parent seems to be distinctly important'... 'The differences between mothers and fathers appear to be much less important than the similarities' and 'What (the) research did not support was the assertion that optimal child adjustment demands that every child have a father in the home".*
Prof. Michael E. Lamb *(1).*

## 7.1 Building your village

Support networks are going to be crucial when you are bringing up your child or children on your own. However, ensuring that these networks are in place and solid enough to ease you through every trial and challenge ahead is not easy. The more diverse the elements you can gather around you, the more robust they will be.

With any luck, the foundations of your village will be in place by the time you have your baby – through your antenatal classes, NCT or other pre-birth activities, if not through family or friends with small children. If your baby arrived early or you moved to a new area just before the birth, you still need to start building these networks as soon as you are up to it. It might be a little harder working around your baby's needs and schedule, when you are probably at your most tired and vulnerable. Try not to lose heart or expect too much too quickly, it is a big task but you have time, and it is more important to build up your own resilience than to get everything else sorted right away. Consider activities that will contribute both to your network building and to your relationship with your baby – mother and baby massage or music, buggy runs or exhibitions – whatever you can find in your area. A cinema near me has even started having afternoon showings (of grown-up films) for mums with babes in arms – the latest film for you, an hour and a half of cosy cuddles for the babe, and then a chat with the other mums over a cuppa, how many boxes can you tick in one go?

Try to identify what you need and what you can offer, and find the local resources such as notice boards, newsletters, social media groups or websites – your health visitor or baby clinic should be able to provide some information, but if they don't, you could ask to use their notice board. Nextdoor and Gumtree can be good places to put an ad, for instance for other new mums to do a weekly outing to a play centre, park or museum. If you have a car, you could offer a weekly lift to the supermarket in exchange for a weekly play date / coffee morning. If you like ironing and hate cooking (or vice versa), you could offer a weekly ironing session in exchange for a batch of homemade baby food. Be bold: if it's a swap, people are unlikely to feel you're trying to take advantage, but they may still say no out of shock; we just aren't used to building these links, and it may take a while for others to consider it as a serious proposition, not a threat.

You can also build a virtual village of other solo mums. By making connections with others who are doing or have done the same thing, you will have access to all the experiences and information they have gathered, so you can feel more confident in the choices you are making. You will have a forum where you can explore and develop your ideas and plans. You can develop the habit of offering and looking for support, both emotional and practical. If you are lucky and any of these women live near enough, you can also look forward to being on maternity leave and spending time together with your babies.

Ideally, you will find other mums who are alone at weekends and within reach when those with partners are not free, so you can plan activities to reduce the risk of feeling that you are missing out. The other thing to consider (and raise with your new friends) is the realisation that there is nobody to share the daily joys your baby will bring to your life, no other parent to delight and amuse, and how hard that is.

## 7.2 Developing a new identity

No matter how long you have waited, how well you have planned or how much you have yearned for this, from the moment your child is born, your life will change completely in ways you cannot have imagined. The identity you had in your family, your community and your working life will all be affected. Becoming a mother will change your priorities, your relationships and your everyday options as well as your long-term view of yourself and your life. You cannot know how for sure, but you may as well be prepared for the fact things are going to be in flux.

The first few weeks will be important in giving others the message about how to relate to you. You may be euphoric or wrecked, totally enthralled and engrossed by your baby or barely managing, or all of these at different times. Although it can be hard to think about others at this stage, it is worth trying to create a role so they are there to support you in the future. If nothing else, share your joy with them so they can feel included and connected.

As far as you can, plan for an excess of support for the first few weeks of your baby's life. You'll probably be elated but exhausted by the birth, and wanting to put everything you have into getting to know your baby, to establish good feeding and sleeping, even before you get home from the hospital (if that's where you gave birth). Even though you just want to focus on your baby, people will want to help. If the time is not right, practice graceful ways of telling people you are just trying to get the baby to latch on or you have poo up to your elbows, but PLEASE ring back or pop by later... and if they could stop by the shop for another bag of wipes or nappies, that would be great! Every time you feel like taking the phone off the hook or ignoring a message, remind yourself that the time you really need someone it will be that much harder to ask, if all you have done before is rebuff the offers. Of course, if there was no choice, you would find a way to manage, but there is no need to make yourself prove this if you do not have to! Thus, your new identity must always include the awareness of the future for the two of you, and the vast potential of circumstances.

The need for support and reliance on others is not the only way your identity is likely to change. If nothing else, the amount of energy that mothering will take will leave you less able than you used to be to keep up with perfectly ordinary things. Give yourself time; don't feel you need to work it all out now, because things will continue to change for quite some time. Babies' needs change from day to day, week to week, month to month, and every time you adapt, the next stage will be imminent and requiring further adjustments. The cycle of feeling lost, getting on top of it all, and suddenly realising that it is all changing again can feel exhausting and bewildering at the same time as delightful and exciting. The best you can do is to remember it is all to be expected and perfectly normal, and there are probably alternative ways of dealing with anything that is not working, the trick is to find the stamina and initiative. Rest is the one critical ingredient.

Another factor as a solo mum is that there is nowhere to escape when you need time out, nobody to console you, take over or be a 'second point of view' when things get rough. There is no way out, you have to find a way of dealing with it. Set clear precedents like 'When mummy says 'I need five minutes peace' or a bath, or a phone call, you have to go and see what is on telly (and you can take the biscuit tin / fruit bowl with you)', or something that is usually a treat. It is important not to let it come across as the child being punished because of your mood. Similarly, for a child who is liable to tantrums, you need to find a way of keeping them safe while they calm down and holding on to your own needs until it's passed.

Your sense of identity comes from the inside as well as the outside: do not forget to congratulate yourself for the ability to adapt and learn from the changes you are facing. Your confidence is an essential ingredient in what you have to offer your child, including the confidence that you will find the resources you need to deal with whatever comes.

### 7.3 Returning to work

Returning to work can also be a big part of developing your new identity, especially in terms of remembering who you are other than a mum. You may have worked out your plans for balancing work with a baby before you even became pregnant, or you may have left it until you cannot ignore it anymore. In either case, be prepared for your perceptions to change as your pregnancy progresses and after you have been at home with your baby full-time.

> *I always assumed I'd have to work full-time again eventually, but returned half-time after a year's maternity leave, and actually never went back full-time at all. I increased my hours and changed my work pattern a few times – for instance my manager accepted me working four days a week in term-time and two days a week in the school holidays, I just had to show that the hours added up over the year. It's always worth asking!*
>
> *Ellie, mum to Tom, London*

Many employers will offer a graduated return to work, though this may involve using the annual leave accrued while you were away. You have a right to ask for part-time and flexible work, and your employer has to consider this reasonably, although they are not obliged to agree to your request. Remember that the one *absolute* certainty is that the way you live will change once you are a mother, and your spending needs will change accordingly.

**Childcare**

Childcare is a big worry for all working mothers. The

available resources can vary wildly depending on where you live. Your local authority should have information about local childminders and nurseries they have inspected and approved, and may also have some direct provision. Your local NCT group may also be a good source of information, as will your baby clinic and health visitor. Good childcare is always in short supply, and many childcare settings have long waiting lists, so start looking around as soon as you can to get an idea of what's available and make a note of what the waiting lists are like so you don't limit your choices. If you're stuck, you may need to find one service for the first few months while you are waiting for a place in the setting of your choice.

The pros and cons of different childcare provisions are very personal. Some women don't like the idea of too many people being involved in their baby's care, as in a nursery, others don't want a family setting to compete with the child's own home. Whatever your choice, it is crucial for you to feel that your child is safe and happy if you are going to be comfortable returning to work and able to focus on your job. Arrange to spend time with your child in the new childcare setting so you get an idea of what they will be doing during the day, and get to know the staff - the ones who provide the hands-on care as well as the managers and those who are in charge. It is reasonable to expect returning to work and leaving your baby in the care of others to be stressful and worrying, but overall you should be able to relax after the first few days and feel contented within a few weeks. It will help if you have built up a basis of trust and understanding beforehand.

### 7.4 Finances

For most of us, making the decision to have a baby is part of a bigger plan to change life, to change the focus of our professional and social life to a more child and family-centred lifestyle. Many of us make radical changes in our work when we start a family, often reducing our hours to have more time, or changing career and re-training for something that is more family friendly. These changes are likely to result in reduced income, counterbalanced by giving you more time and energy.

There is no denying that raising a child will make demands on your budget as well as reducing your flexibility to increase your earnings. Money Supermarket (2) estimates the cost of raising a child in 2018 is £64,071 for a boy and £93,771 for a girl for the first 18 years, the difference mostly being in the cost of girls' toiletries and clothes. Wiki (3) puts it at around £230,000 per child. And then there's the cost of higher education... so there's no escaping it, most of us will have to make radical changes to meet these costs within our incomes.

One change for those on UC has been an increased allowance for childcare costs, in view of the fact that UC is meant to make it always pay to be in work. In some areas, the actual cost of a nursery place is so much higher than the allowance that some parents will not be able to cover the difference...

The first thing is to note that it's probably not going to be as bad as it sounds, since there are so many ways in which your spending patterns will change – meals out, entertainment and travel will inevitably be curtailed, but the cost of childcare can be jaw-dropping, and there's no bulk discount if you happen to have twins.

There are many guides to family finance with suggestions for keeping the costs down, and most of this information will be on a local level: look out for nursery and school notices about sales of children's clothes and toys, which are more often grown out of than worn out.

*I don't have very much money and have to live in one room (I rent out the other room for some extra income). It's not ideal but it certainly helps. Since being lucky enough to have my baby, my ideals have changed. I would rather walk around in rags and not buy myself anything, as what I now have is priceless.*

*I think money worries and health worries will always be there and never go away, but the chance to have a baby will only come around once.*

*Alyssa, London*

Benefits for working parents come in two formats, either cash payments such as Child Benefit or additions to Income Support, Job Seekers Allowance or Universal Credit (UC), or as exemptions such as free prescriptions, dental treatment and travel concessions. The Benefits system is in turmoil at the time of writing, with the UC roll-out slowed down again so that claimants in some regions will still be on the old patchwork of benefits until 2023.

There is some hope that the UC system will be abandoned or at least radically changed, as it has been fraught with difficulties. There are caps for housing costs and the number of children for whom you can claim (usually two), and an overall cap per household, so you may face radical changes if you are moving on to benefits

There are situations where you may lose more than you gain if you move from Job Seekers Allowance or Income Support to UC, so it is important to get expert advice. You can use the websites of Citizens Advice, Turn2Us or Gingerbread (4, 5, 6), or visit your nearest advice centre for the latest situation in your area.

## 7.5 Raising an only child

The survey I conducted (see appendix 1) shows that most of us will become mothers at an older than average age and so may not pursue a second pregnancy. Unless you were yourself the only child of a single mother, it is likely that you had to share your mother with others – siblings and / or a father / second parent. In a family of two, you may find that the relationship with your child is more intense than in a larger family, and wonder how that might affect your child. There is nothing inherently wrong with an intense relationship, but we should be aware that it carries certain risks. Most of the times the relationship will probably be intensely good, but inevitably there will be moments when it isn't, so it's important to pay attention to the detail.

In a family with one adult and one child, the child will not observe how to negotiate differences from a safe distance, as they will be directly involved in any conflict. They will not necessarily have direct experience of the way everyday rows blow over between siblings, or of how two adults resolve a difference of opinion and manage complex decisions.

We can address this by finding opportunities to help them learn. When they start nursery or school, we can talk about the fact that making friends and getting on with others can be difficult, and that it can help to talk about it. We can take opportunities to point out how people deal with differences and conflict, and we can discuss the different responses and consequences. We can teach our children the language to recognise and deal with these issues, so they know what is going on when they meet them in real life. Explain that the quiet child may be shy or fearful, or the angry child may be frightened, so your child can deal with them with understanding and compassion rather than taking it personally. If these are new ideas for you, you can learn more from books such as Faber and Mazlich (7).

> *I remember when my son started school: he came home one day and said he'd had a row with his best friend. He was so upset, he thought that was the end of the friendship. dealing with conflict or letting things blow over. His friend had three younger siblings, so was well used to disagreements being forgotten by the following day...*
>
> *It took a lot or reassurance, but he came back from school the next day and told me it had never been mentioned...*
>
> *Ellie, mum to Tom, London*

These opportunities arise in everyday life around us as well as in the stories and films we share with our kids. We can use all sorts of events to draw out observations of how people dealt with a problem, ask your child what they think might happen next or how they might have dealt with it.

Given that your child will have only one other person in the household, it is all the more important to b e able to talk about how you relate to each other, to discuss interactions and give them the language to understand the processes. If you can look back on a row and identify the feelings on both sides, it will make it easier to de-fuse next time, to recall that we can talk it through and it will blow over, that it's OK to feel grumpy or disagree, things will go back to normal afterwards. If you can deconstruct incidents of successful interaction, that's even better: talk through your daily routine for getting out of the house or getting back at the end of the day and identify what makes it go smoothly, so your child learns how to appreciate their own role in the routines. Point out how proud you are that they know where to find things or put them away, praise them for learning to do buttons and laces and explain how good you feel that you can trust them to help things run smoothly.

The classic British stiff upper lip / stoical silence are not a useful response to distressing situations in an intense two-person family. It is much better to face the stresses and provide our children with the language and tools to ride them out. I believe that a child who can identify and name their own feelings will become more sensitive to others' feelings, and more able to manage relationships.

### 7.6 Twins and multiples

There is no point in playing down the fact that having

twins or multiples is difficult, and all the more so if you don't have anyone around to help. For obvious reasons, no mums of twins have responded to my requests for tips / suggestions: you won't have a moment to spare for a long time, and if you do, you will have plenty of other priorities, if not just sleep!

However, there are some good support networks in place through the Twins & Multiple Birth Association (TAMBA), who also have a single mums section (8). Your health visitor should be able to point you in the right direction for all kinds of help, for instance some courses for nursery nurses put their students on placement with new mums of twins. They will have been checked by the Disclosure and Barring Service (DBS) and supervised, and although it is not intended for them to be a 'mothers' help' or nanny, they will definitely be an extra pair of hands.

If you've got the money to pay for help, you need to work out what will be the most useful support. It may be that you choose to have someone do the housework, laundry or cooking to free you up to put your energy into the children, or to take them out for a regular break to allow you to sleep for four unbroken hours.

You also need to consider their 'twin-ness' – will you want to treat them as a pair, dress them the same etc., or do you want emphasise their differences? Most likely both of these will be appropriate at times, and the twins will let you know how they feel about their relationship too. Some schools have a policy to separate twins in different classes, to make sure they can develop their own identity. If you feel that would not suit your children, you need to check (or challenge) the policy before applying for a school place.

### 7.7 Trying for two or more...

An increasing number of solo mums decide to have a second or subsequent child, either because they have age on their side or because they decide to use the higher tech fertility treatments that simply did not exist until recently.

I cannot voice enough respect for those who go ahead, there are many advantages of having brothers and sisters and of raising a brood of siblings. This section, however, focuses more on the practicalities of having more than one child.

Part of the planning will have to include a consideration of the realities. From finding care for your first child while you attend the appointments involved in conceiving the second, to ensuring your existing child still gets all their needs met, to finding the energy during pregnancy, and having resources in case there are problems; it's going to be a big job. My mother assured me that it was much easier having me and my brother within thirteen months of each other than the longer gaps between my other siblings, but that was in the context of not working and having ample help and support. Your kids may grow up with a built-in best friend / mentor, but they might also fight and resent each other, and in the early days their needs are bound to make far greater and often conflicting demands on you than a single child would.

Bear in mind the greater risks with a pregnancy when you are older and the chance you may need to be admitted to hospital before the actual birth. Make sure you have flexible and simple arrangements made the pregnancy, or having to rearrange everything from your hospital bed.

One woman I know was told at her seven-month antenatal appointment that she needed to be admitted immediately due to life-threatening pre-eclampsia. A friend collected her three-year-old from nursery as her backup carer was away on holiday and she ended up having to use a social services emergency fostering placement until she had hired an au pair, using Skype from her hospital bed. The au pair moved into her flat and helped the friend with whom the toddler stayed, ferrying kids to different schools, laundry, getting the little one to visit mum in hospital and so on. The scenario turned out okay in the end, but it was not much fun at the time. I hope that your emergency provisions will never be required, but they need to be there just in case.

## 7.8 Raising kids without a dad

Single women who have chosen to have a family their own have generally prepared conscientiously for the child coming into their life and look upon it as a positive choice rather than an unfortunate outcome. They also tend to avoid the disadvantages stereotypically associated with single parents such as poverty, young maternal age, poor education, housing and support, and isolation. On the whole, single mothers 'by choice' will be more mature, stable, resourceful, well off and better educated than average. They will have put considerable thought into their decision, weighed up the pros and cons and made practical changes in preparation. Crucially, they have not been let down or abandoned and can focus freely on their child's needs without the emotional baggage of an absent partner and / or lost relationship in the immediate background.

Conflict and strife are a common feature of homes where parents are separating, and there is strong evidence of the damage this causes to children. However, after these factors are accounted for, there is no evidence that the lack of a father is associated with disadvantage or negative outcomes for children.

The main study of the families of women who have chosen solo motherhood is by the Cambridge Centre for Family Research. At this stage, the results show little difference between our children and any others, and where there are differences, our children tend to do better than average (9, 10). These studies are small, and the socio-economic profile of our families probably accounts for at least some of this distinction. However, there is no evidence that our children are disadvantaged by the absence of a father in the family in any way.

An interesting observation from DCN workshops (11) is that often women who did not have a positive relationship with a father figure find it harder to consider what support their donor-conceived child may need in respect of any sense of loss. To put it simply, those who did not enjoy a relationship with a traditional father figure won't necessarily feel that their child is lacking something important, while those who did may worry that their child is missing out on something that they value in their own history. But missing out on something does not necessarily mean missing it: I didn't have grandparents or an extended family, but I didn't miss them. People have told me that this must have been a loss, but I simply didn't experience it as such. It is just a different experience.

All families are different, but most children believe that their own family is the norm, at least until they are school-aged. Is there something that fathers contribute to families and to child development in particular and, if so, how can solo mums ensure their children don't miss out?

I asked friends who work in the field of child development and welfare and family and child psychotherapy, and was loaned several books I was assured would provide the latest data, but I did not find evidence of anything that only fathers can contribute. I did find evidence that fathers are capable of providing all the aspects of parenting that conventionally come from mothers. Ruth Feldman (2010) (12) found that fathers who had the same amount of close contact with their babies had raised levels of the hormone oxytocin and developed the same 'bonded' relationship as do mothers. Rather than reinforce the need for a father, this evidence seems to suggest that gender is irrelevant and, as found by Professor Lamb (1), it is the loving relationship that counts. Of course two loving parents can offer more than one, and three even more, but the evidence clearly shows that when all other factors are equal, a solo mother can raise a child just as successfully as a couple.

The things that we might perceive that a father does or contributes are based on gender stereotypes, and can in fact be done by women – whether it's fixing a bike, naming the parts of a backhoe loader, or getting furniture moved. What is harder to do alone is to find the stamina, good humour and equanimity that parenting and thinking through decisions and concerns demand.

Most of the issues we face raising our children single-handedly will be exactly the same as in other types of families. In fact, many of us have heard friends with partners complain that it would be easier not to have that second adult when they make the lack of a father in the home will become a significant negative.

Of course, not having a father in the home does not mean that our children will not have any examples, and if we can find men to act as role models, we can at least ensure they've got good examples to counterbalance the stereotypes in the world around us. If you can ask a relative or friend, you could organise regular times for them to spend together – to do typical 'masculine' things you that are not easy for you, do as well as to do the untypical, bedtime stories, cooking a meal, to provide a well-rounded model of adulthood. No child can have too many such models in their life. I never succeeded in recruiting such a person myself, but I made the effort to notice and mention all the good examples I saw around us. The bottom line is that diverse experience is a good thing in itself. Children are naturally curious and exploratory, so you may find they gravitate towards men in social gatherings.

Don't read too much into the fact they may try out the word 'daddy' on men: any woman who works in a nursery will tell you that most kids will call her 'mummy' at some time. It does not mean they're lacking a mum at home, it's just because most women in their lives are mums, and the men in their friends' lives are often 'daddy', they have yet to learn that it's an exclusive relationship.

One concern I have for the children in our families is that they will not have any direct experience of two adults negotiating the everyday minutiae of life and of resolving their differences. This might leave them poorly equipped for the future, when they have to manage in their own households, relationships and families. We therefore need to pay attention to all the unspoken and subconscious processes going on, and to try to bring them out in the open to make sure they are learning. They can be involved, for instance, when we prioritise the housework and shopping or organise an outing, or make decisions such as choosing a birthday card or piece of clothing, or deciding what to eat for dinner.

We have to ensure that our children are aware of the processes that would routinely be discussed and negotiated between parents and not grow up thinking they just 'happen' without grasping the meaning.

This means involving them in decision making and giving them responsibility so they develop a sense of agency in their world – but without making them feel more responsible than is age-appropriate. And we need to expose our children as much as possible to different ways of living and to people managing, and relationships constructively, so they learn that there are different ways of getting things right. It helps if we can point out the features, the strengths and implications, for instance how families deal with a move, a new baby or a bereavement.

**Our own feelings about men and fathers:**

Before having my son, I went through a process that

may be familiar to others. When I faced my disappointment at not having a partner with whom to start a family in the ordinary way, I initially felt I must be doing something wrong, and went through the painful process of trying a bit harder. After a few more disappointments, I started feeling angry at men for not being on the same page as me, and at the world for letting them get away with it. Eventually, I came round to accepting that I had better just go ahead, confident I had a lot to offer and could do a decent job of it.

When I was pregnant, I faced the possibility that I might have a boy. In retrospect, I really do not know how I had never thought of this before, but it was a shock and led to some serious thinking. I realised that I must make sure any boy I brought up should know that being a boy and growing into a man and a father was great and good. I would want any daughter of mine to grow up trusting that being a girl and a woman was wonderful (as well as that she had every chance of meeting a person who'd want to have babies with her, if she chose to have children).

After years of sitting round with my women friends taking apart our relationships with potential partners, both real and hoped for, and bemoaning the fact they so rarely came up to scratch, I would have to stop and NEVER let my child hear any of this stereotyped denigration of half the human population – not from me, anyway. Instead, I would have to make the effort to notice and point out every good thing about men that came across my radar, to make sure my child would have a good idea of how to be (and recognise) a good man. No doubt I have missed many opportunities, but I have tried hard. And if my son is any evidence, I have done a good enough job, even without an 'in-house' model.

I think it is important for us to come to terms with our situation and not let feelings of inadequacy, guilt or blame get in the way. Of course, we can recognise that life might be better with a dad or partner in the family (and money in the bank account and roses over the front door), but we must also feel confident that we can and will provide for all our children's needs adequately, and prepare responsibly for the challenges and eventualities. Counselling and therapy can help in this respect, as can good friends and family. The best defence is a good support network, preferably one that includes other families with a similar set-up, so that our children know it is ordinary and unremarkable to manage in different circumstances, rather than feel defined by their fatherlessness.

Once our children appear, it is more than likely that they will at one stage or another wish for a dad, and we need to make space for them to express their own feelings. We have to respond both sympathetically and constructively. We must acknowledge our children's feelings – by accepting them and reassuring them that it is ok to be sad. This will be harder if you are still feeling guilty. We can reassure our children that it's OK by getting on their level, for instance by encouraging them to imagine what they'd do if they had a dad, what a dad would do with them. If you can then find ways of meeting those needs, great, but if you can't, don't beat yourself up, just support them kindly, as you would if they wished for a trip to the moon or a swim with dolphins. Several of us have had running bedtime talks with our children about what they would have done with a dad, as others have about fantasy friends: join in the game and legitimise it by enjoying it (you would like to be there too and share the fun), do not let it build up into a private tragedy.

## 7.9 Preparing for the empty nest, eventually

When you're struggling to keep your head above the parapet in the first few years of motherhood, it's hard to remember that your child will grow up and most likely become so independent that they will move out, leave home, be gone... and you will be able to pick up on life as it was, or develop an entirely new one. I have written about my own experience in appendix 5, but at some stage, you can start thinking about what you will do when the time comes that you are no longer needed as full-time mum. Of course, some children may not be able to manage total independence, perhaps due to a disability, but you will nevertheless have changing patterns of duties – to support them in placements, in training and in work.

It's really worth considering what kind of a life you want, because it might be a brilliant opportunity for change and new directions, and the better prepared you are the simpler it will be. If your retirement coincides with your child becoming an adult, it presents even more opportunities. Big changes require planning, so go for it: let your dreams guide you towards the fulfilment you will lose as your children move away. It could be a physical move, a career change or return to education, or a fresh start in something completely new.

It is important not to allow your child's needs to restrict you anymore. Don't get caught in the myth that they will be indebted by further education unless you bail them out.

Yes, you may still be of the generation where higher education was really free, but the present arrangements are such that the repayments are not prohibitive (13), and most people never pay all the funding back.

It is important to move on from your dreams of how family life was supposed to be if you are going to build contentment and pride in the family you have. It's important also to move on from the all-consuming task of parenting in order to allow your child to grow up, as well as enabling yourself to move on to the next phase of your life with contentment and fulfilment. We would be doing them no favours if we expected to continue the same level of involvement, and we would probably be guaranteeing ourselves frustration and disappointment. On the other hand, we can also be looking at preparing for a time when we might need support ourselves and how to find it without turning to our children.

## References

1. Lamb, M.: The Role of the Father in Child Development, Wiley, 2010
2. www.moneysupermarket.com/life-insurance/cost-of-raising-a-child/
3.en.wikipedia.org/wiki_Cost_of_raising_a_child#/United_Kingdom
4.CitizensAdvice:www.citizensadvice.org.uk/benefits
5.Turn2Us:www.turn2us.org.uk/Your-Situation/Bringing-up-a-child
6.Gingerbread: www.gingerbread.org.uk/information/benefits-tax-credits-and-universal-credit/benefit-calculators/benefit-calculator/
7.Faber, A. and Mazlich, E.: How to Talk So Kids Will Listen & Listen So Kids will Talk, Harper Collins, 2012
8.Twins & Multiple Birth Association (TAMBA) www.tamba.org.uk/Support/One-Parent-Families
9.Golombok, S.: Parenting: what really counts? Routledge, 2000
10.Golombok, S.: Modern Families: Parents and Children in New Family Forms, Cambridge UP, 2015
11.Fine, K. (ed): Donor Conception for Life, Karnac,2015 - Chapter 4 by Fine, K. and Mitchell, T.: Family of Choice
12.Feldman, R.: Fathers' Oxytocin Levels Develop Through Close Contact and Contribute to Bonding just as with Mothers www.sciencedaily.com/releases/2010/08/100820101207.htm
13.Student finance: www.moneysavingexpert.com/students

# Chapter 8: How do the children fare?

*"...young adults (...) from female-headed households showed lower levels of anxiety, depression, hostility and problematic alcohol use than their counterparts from traditional families, and higher levels of self-esteem, indicating more positive psychological adjustment among young adults who had grown up in solo and lesbian mother homes..."* Golombok and Badger, 2010.

## 8.1 Bringing the child's needs to the fore

> *It took me a long time to accept the idea that being a single parent was fair on a child and also that so little information about the donor would be available. I found the first clinic I attended did not make the donor's note to the child available before making a choice, which is not a requirement of the HFEA. For this reason and many others, I changed to treatment at an NHS hospital, and this made an enormous difference to my experience, which was much more positive.*
>
> *Anon.*

Once the decision has been made to have a child on our own, and while undergoing treatment, our focus will mainly be on achieving a successful pregnancy. Concerns about whether we can offer our children everything they need as a solo parent will probably linger at the back of our minds, raising doubts every now and then, but not coming back to the forefront until the baby has arrived safely.

When you have decided to go ahead, it is important to consider your child's future needs, not just your own.

- Join a support group for single women in your area, or get one started so that you can share experiences, thoughts, questions. If you are lucky, it will continue to provide a community where your children will know families like their own.
- Join the DCN and talk with single women who are raising donor-conceived children about how they made their decisions and what life is like in a solo mum family. The DCN run valuable workshops and conferences, and produce booklets that can you give an insight into how children change in their understanding of their beginnings as they grow up. The DCN also provide a staff-run helpline for members to discuss all aspects of donor conception and parenting, and they can point you towards other relevant sources of support and information when needed.
- Read accounts from donor-conceived adults about how they feel about their origins. Note the differences between those whose parents seemed comfortable with their decisions and were open with their children from the start, and those who only learned of their donor conception later in life. Stories can be found on the DCN website, and in various books, blogs and websites listed in the Bibliography. Remember that most of the adult offspring will have unknown donors as they will have been conceived before 2005.

## 8.2 What do children need?

There is a myriad of theories about parenting, but there are three main models:

- Social learning theories suggest that the child's development is shaped by their experience with people and the world around them.
- Attachment theory suggests that it is the quality of the relationship with the caregiver that determines how the child will develop.
- Parenting style theories suggest that the specific nature of the warmth and control shown by parents / carers will determine how the child develops.

Professor Michael Lamb (1) is a world expert on what children need and often acts as an expert witness in court proceedings such as custody disputes. He has reviewed hundreds of studies of child development from many different perspectives, looking at which features in families correlated with positive child adjustment. He established that it is the *quality* of parenting that matters to the development of children, not how many parents they have. The gender and sexual orientation of their carers is also irrelevant.

The relationships between carer and child, between carers and other significant adults, consistent and confident parenting, and the adequacy of resources such as stimulation, care, warmth and encouragement, have the most significant impact on positive child adjustment. He concludes that the negative consequences for children in one-parent families are to do with abandonment, strife, and instability. Children born to single parents by choice will be relatively protected from these unless they exist in the extended family or support network, or with future partners.

He also identifies poverty as a risk to children's development, and we have to recognise that the changes in the UK social welfare system will not be providing the resources we grew up to expect. I wish there was robust evidence that material poverty can be counterbalanced by a determination to provide our children with stimulation and self-respect, but this is another area where research has not kept up with social change. Hunger, homelessness and health hazards are critical, but expensive holidays, the latest fashion, gadget or home entertainment can all be replaced by simpler resources and at no cost to self-esteem or well-being.

**Stability**

Of course physical stability is important. Children need to know that they have a safe and secure place to live and space to call their own, and that they will be fed and looked after, but emotional stability is also vital. The evidence from transient communities suggests that harm from physical instability can be overcome if the child has strong and consistent emotional bonds. As solo mums, it is almost easier for us to ensure that our children have a constant and consistent source of emotional support.

However, there will be times when we need to leave our children with others, whether in a formal or an informal environment. It is essential that we have confidence in the people who will be caring for our children so that they can respond appropriately to their emotional needs. We should be trying to maintain a steady number of caregivers. The evidence from Lamb's research suggests that children can cope with different styles of caring, what matters is that carers should trust and respect each other. If your children pick up negative vibes from you about a childminder or, for that matter, about grandparents or a babysitter, it can undermine their own trust, and the relationships may be affected.

**Safety**
Children need us to look out for their physical well-being as they develop the skills to look after themselves. We need to manage and pre-empt their need for safety while also helping them develop their own awareness. In the long run, we need to resist the temptation to be overprotective, and allow them to learn from mistakes in order to develop responsibility for their own personal safety. We may be tempted to compensate for being the sole parent, but it is just as important for them to learn to regulate themselves as for other children.

**Stimulation**
Children need stimulation in order to learn and develop. They need to be exposed to a variety of experiences to give them opportunities to find their own interests and preferences, so even if you have little interest, for instance, in sport or music or fashion, make the effort to expose your children to new experiences, to allow them to find their passion.

Our attitudes will have a strong influence, so we should make sure we are not conveying reluctance or negative feelings. Children who are by nature cautious or shy may need extra support to get out into the world and feel at home in it, even if they do not all turn into gregarious extroverts and adventurers.

Consider the different people involved in your child's life and how they might be enhancing it: do not be afraid to seek help – for instance asking a grandparent to foster your child's interest in pets or the garden. This is not to say you constantly need to offer activities to your child.

They also need to learn to entertain themselves, or to help out, while you are doing the laundry or preparing dinner. It will strengthen their autonomy and self-reliance.

It's important for children to be involved from the start in the ordinary processes of daily life, and to play a part appropriate to their age and ability, and taking the time to help children learn the skills they need to help out at home will pay off in the long run when they see this as a natural part of their day. They can be involved in all aspects of family life, but that does not mean that life should revolve around them. It is important for them to learn about everyday life, including the boring necessities, and if possible, they can learn to enjoy getting things done together, but if they feel that it all depends on them, they will soon back off from responsibility that is beyond their ability.

**Acceptance of difference**

We can work on this long before our children arrive. Consider how you will help your child learn that people can be different in many ways, while fundamentally being very similar, and that 'normal' does not mean 'the same', particularly if you live in an area without much diversity.

You can talk about this with your child when looking at picture books and stories, as well as in the street, the park, at school or in social surroundings. Describe the groupings you see around you and compare them, trying to bring out the similarities and the positives. Importantly, do not ignore the father figures that they will see in many family settings: explain and explore them, so that they understand the relationship even if they do not have it themselves. Their growing understanding of life's diversity will help their confidence if someone points out or queries their family set up, or when someone does not understand their situation, and they may learn to accept the curiosity of others without feeling vulnerable.

Encourage your children to understand that change and difference are good – for instance, it would be so boring if everyone wore blue all the time, and if you never tried anything new, you might never have found out how much you like caramel ice cream!

**Resilience**
This is the ability to face and overcome a challenge, to bounce back. Much as we would like the world to be kind to our children, we would be doing them a disservice if we did not help them understand how to deal with adversity. Some of this resilience may come from personality, but it can certainly be developed and reinforced. For instance, it has been established (2) that having goals and a sense of purpose provide a strong basis for resilience, as will a network of good relationships.

We can recognise and value our children's friendships, which will strengthen them, and we can encourage our children to pursue their goals and ambitions without adding too much pressure that may take away the enjoyment, and we can reinforce their identity by valuing their choices. For instance we could get into the habit of asking what they hope ('What will make you happy / good / proud?') for an upcoming event or activity, and asking afterwards what was good / best. Other helpful insights can be found in the writing of Dr Laura Markham on 'mastery' (3), and Angela Duckworth on 'grit' (4). These concepts are not without

controversy, but they can help us identify where our children might need support.
Children who are more self-aware and can name their own needs and ask for help will be better able to meet challenges, as will children who develop problem-solving skills. This can be encouraged on an everyday basis by allowing our children to work things out for themselves.

Even toddlers can be encouraged to think ahead and work out, for example, whether wearing their favourite canvas shoes will be practical when it is raining. Helping them to recognise and name their feelings such as frustration, fear, excitement will help them to manage them. Over time, they'll develop this skill for themselves, enabling them to figure out how much homework they'll need to finish by Friday if they want to go out for the day on Saturday, or how they might earn the money to buy something they want, or to find the recipe, check the cupboard and write the shopping list for the meal they want when a friend comes to tea. Younger children will feel more confident trying again to tie a shoelace or putting the book back onto the bookshelf if they have faced frustration and succeeded with encouragement before; if they know the words, they can talk themselves through the process.

## 8.3 Our children's developing identity

Identity is a varied and complex part of our make-up. It includes our physical and psychological characteristics (gender, height, eye colour, personality etc.), our strengths and interests (athletic, artistic, animal loving) as well as environmental and social factors such as class, ethnicity, family and other relationships. It provides us with a sense of our uniqueness as well as of belonging, a sense of 'self' in relation to others.Our identity evolves throughout life and may be context-dependent. For instance, it is normal to feel or behave differently when you are at work to when you are with family or friends. Experiences will influence our sense of identity, but on the whole, there will be consistent tendencies, a 'personality' that is apparent in different settings and over time.

**Genetics and identity**

When considering how donor conceived adults feel about how their conception has influenced their identity, remember that those who are adults now will most likely have been conceived using anonymous donors, and be unable to access information about their genetic heritage.

*Although he is happy in the knowledge that I used a sperm donor, he doesn't relate to the donor conceived 'community'. He isn't rejecting it either – it's just that I don't think at the moment he feels he needs it.*

*Sue, mother of a wonderful son, 15,*
*Through donor insemination via a London clinic*

There are donor-conceived adults who express distress at not knowing part of their genetic make-up, and the damage they feel it has done to their sense of identity (5). Some even campaign for donor conception to be banned on the grounds of child protection. However, bear in mind many do not share this experience as a loss, and feel their parent(s) provided a good grounding. They do not feel that genetic knowledge is an essential component for healthy development, and have no need to be as vocal. If it is rare to read positive stories of growing up as donor conceived, it is not because they do not exist, but because they are not felt to be interesting enough to be told. The people in this category just feel it is their normality.

Overall, being donor conceived will only be one aspect of our children's identity, even if at some stages it may feel more important than others. As they grow and understand the different implications, there will be periods when they need to ask questions and explore their feelings, while at others, they will forget, just as they will find that others lose interest and even forget, once they've got used to it.

**Being different and fitting in:**
In 'Far from the Tree' Andrew Solomon (6) writes about how families adapt to having a child who does not 'fit' in one way or another. Although much of his research focuses on disability, the results and theories can be applied to donor conception. He suggests that identity has two dimensions.

The vertical dimension comes from family and society through the generations, whereas the horizontal dimension comes from peer groups and finding a community of those like you. So toddlers may have a good sense of their family, but when they start going to nursery or school, they will also develop a sense of themselves as 'In class 1' or one of the 'skipping rope group' or 'on the red table' for reading.

Solomon interviews families in depth and finds that there has been a trend since the middle of the last century towards greater acceptance of difference both within families and by society. Solomon repeatedly notes the enrichment that this has brought to the families and individuals concerned. His main thesis is that 'Fixing is the illness model, acceptance is the identity model.' In other words, accepting difference allows children to belong and feel integrated, rather than to feel they need to adapt to the 'norm'. Solomon is himself gay and the father of donor-conceived children. He describes the importance of building links across peer groups to help overcome any potential feelings of isolation due to 'difference' and to build up resilience.

Anja Karnein, in her essay, 'Parenthood: whose right is it anyway?' (7), discusses the conventional claim that a genetic link is necessary to 'root' the child in its family and provide an identity. She concludes that there is no basis to deny the right to parenthood to those who cannot achieve it in the conventional manner. Non-biological parents (e.g. adoptive) are just as capable of bringing up children who flourish.

### 8.4 Fatherless children

Much of the research on delinquency remarks on the incidence in relation to what used to be called 'broken homes', leading the researchers to conclude that fatherlessness causes delinquency. The term broken homes fell out of use because it was felt to be too negative, but I am using it here to emphasise that it was what happened in the home that was damaging, not who was present or absent. If we look at the building blocks of well-adjusted young people as identified by M. E. Lamb (1), we can see that strife and tension that causes the damage. Children need to be able to trust their parents to prioritise their needs; to be there and provide for them. When parents' resources and energy are being absorbed by discord, children feel neglected and unsure where to turn for reassurance or guidance. Even the youngest child reacts when there is ill-feeling between their carers, and feels insecure themselves as a result.

In terms of modelling, there is more assumption than evidence that boys need a male role model. One of the few studies looking at boys who grow up without a father from the start was done by Susan Golombok's team (8), who found remarkably little difference in the development of boys in all-female households. Peggy Drexler (9) considered the 'prevailing wisdom that claims that boys who grow up without fathers turn out to be helpless sissies, violent adults, or gay'. Instead, she found that boys raised without men in the family did not experience any significantly greater gender difficulty, nor did they turn into less 'masculine' men, in terms of their interests and sense of identity. As mothers we can only hope to counteract the pressure on our sons to adopt the more toxic aspects of masculinity that are prevalent around them in society generally.

Of the many studies claiming to prove that men's role is critical in the family or, specifically, married and cohabiting parents, a number are funded by radical Christian groups in the USA such as the Family Research Council, who oppose many aspects of modern life including contraception, divorce, gay rights and working mothers. For an alternative review of the evidence, see de Paolo (10, 11). She clearly demonstrates how the obsolete stereotypes harm the children of single parents, not their mothers or absent fathers.

Similar issues prevail with studies of fatherless girls; the factors that may cause problems have not been identified, and may well be linked to abandonment and stress on the remaining parents, more than the absence of a father. Far from blaming mothers our society needs to ensure that all carers, including mothers, get the support they need to raise their children in a safe, stable and stimulating environment and free of restrictive expectations, irrespective of whether there is a partner in the household.

## References


1. Lamb, M.: The Role of the Father in Child Development, New York Wiley, 2010
2. Seligman, M.: The Optimistic Child, Harper, 1996
3. www.psychologytoday.com/gb/blog/peaceful-parents-happy-kids/201506/12-ways-raise-competent-confident-child-grit
4. blogs.edweek.org/edweek/learning_deeply/2015/04/the_problem_with_grit.html
5. www.mindingmatters.com/one-legacy-of-anonymous-sperm-donation
6. Solomon, A.: Far from the Tree, Scribner, New York, 2012
7. Karnein, A.: Parenthood: Whose Right is it Anyway? in Richards, M., Pennings, G. and Appleby J. (eds): Reproductive Donation: Practice, Policy and Bio-ethics, Cambridge UP, 2012
8. Golombok, S.: Modern Families: Parents and Children in New Family Forms, Cambridge UP, 2015
9. Drexler, P.: Raising Boys Without Men, Rodale, 2005
10. de Paolo, B.: Single Parents and their children: the good news no-one tells you, Create Space Publishing, 2015
11. www.psychologytoday.com/blog/living-single/200901/children-single-mothers-how-do-they-really-fare

# Chapter 9: The legal and ethical context.

The UN Convention on the Rights of the Child (UNCRC), 1990:

*Article 8: the right to an identity and to family relationships*

*Article 9: the right to live with your family or maintain relationships if separated*

*Although the UNCRC does not distinguish between genetic and social relatives, it does imply that connection between relatives is positive in its own right unless proven otherwise.*

## 9.1 Ethics

The area of rights in the field of assisted conception is fraught with conflict, and it is prudent to be aware of this. When starting the process of creating a family, many are driven by a strong internal yearning. The dream of holding a baby can make it hard to think clearly about the long-term consequences of some of your choices, not least the ones that will affect your future children. Some of the legislation can be frustrating and the conflict between the different rules and regulations across the world can give the impression that they are arbitrary. However, this gives you an even greater responsibility to find your own moral standards and work out the best course of action for yourself and your future family.

There are two basic arguments in moral philosophy that are relevant to the debate on donor conception. The first (deontological) is that any action has an inherent moral value – it is either right or wrong, good or bad.

The second (consequential) is that the value of any action can be judged by its consequences, so if it results in something good, then the action is also good. However, neither of these is as simple as they seem and you can have conflicting values. For instance, you would probably agree that selling babies is wrong, but that paying a donor their expenses to help someone have a baby is not. Also, you would probably agree that even though you really want a baby, you would not be justified in using any means necessary to have one. So while it might feel morally acceptable to spend a lot of money on medical and fertility treatment, it probably wouldn't feel as 'right' to pay someone the same amount to hand over their baby to you.

So how does this relate to legal changes in assisted and donor conception? The protection of donors' anonymity, and general secrecy around the practice of donor conception was common across the world until the 1980s. This fitted with the theory that the ends justify the means, ensuring a good supply of sperm so that people who had trouble conceiving could have families of their own. The best interests of the children simply were not part of the picture.

As the years went on, society changed and parents started to feel uncomfortable about keeping secrets, and their children started to assert their need for and right to information about their origins. Disclosure started to be encouraged as a morally 'good' practice in its own right. The principle that secrecy and anonymity were inherently wrong led to legal changes in the UK in 2005, whereby all donated gametes used in the UK must be identifiable when the child reaches eighteen.

The commercial trade in gametes has thrived in societies such as the USA where market principles are the basis for all social transactions, including health and welfare. In the US, donors are paid for their gametes, and the rate of payment may vary according to the donor's level of education, height, or other 'desirable' factors. This has encouraged donors to promote their 'product' to get a better price, which has on occasion meant exaggeration, concealment, or even lies, in their self-portraits. Additionally, sperm bank customers in the US can pay for extra information about donors, which could lead them to assume that they are getting a full description and indication of factors that will influence their child, when there is no prediction of which parental or grandparental genes may be passed on.

Most people agree it is morally wrong to interfere too much with nature, whereas the theory that the ends justify the means might suggest that people should be allowed to 'choose' whatever they can afford, if there is a market. In the UK, less information is given maybe due of a view that too much detail takes us over the tipping point, where people could believe they are controlling the outcome in a way we know is not possible.

In order to ensure that gametes are donated altruistically, donors in the UK cannot receive payment. Although there is an argument that payment ensures a good supply, this is outweighed by the concern that paying donors might encourage people to donate for the wrong reasons, which could be distressing for a child in future.

As you can see, the two views often exist side by side, and it can be a balancing act for those setting the standards. For instance, even though in the UK we do not pay donors for their gametes, we recognise that they may need some incentive more than just the knowledge they are doing something worthwhile. Therefore, donors are offered ‘compensation’ for their effort, time and expenses. In 2011, a maximum fee of £750 for egg donors and £250 for sperm donors in the UK was fixed. Compensation is a clever term to use – not exactly expenses, but not exactly payment either.

The pressure to obtain sperm and eggs without offering a financial incentive means that donors have to be counselled about the long-term implications of their action, which will be beneficial to the resultant children as well. I tend to favour views that give some priority to the welfare of those not immediately involved in the decision, in this case the future children.

When there is an area of doubt, it is wise to factor in the inherent ethical value of the options, maybe by considering how it might look in a different setting. For example, in the US they stopped collecting blood from prisoners, which was cheaper than paying members of the public to ‘donate’, when they were faced with a high incidence of HIV in recipients because of transfusions. Similarly, clinics may have to abandon the market for sperm and eggs if they are subject to lawsuits from people who feel they were deceived about the quality of the goods they paid for.

Analysing your moral standpoint on certain matters becomes even more important in situations where you may feel more at risk of being judged, such as double or embryo donation, or travelling abroad for treatment. It will help you to feel confident that you have given the issue proper consideration, especially in relation to those who are affected but often disregarded. I am referring here both to the donors and the future children. For example, your children may at some future date wonder why the donor chose to donate.

Donors may also experience consequences from donating – be it in the short term with conditions such as ovarian hyper-stimulation syndrome (OHSS) from egg donation, or in the longer term a curiosity about the possibility of a child who has a biological connection to them, or the role of a future partner. These possibilities have practical implications in how you go about your quest for a family. They can lead you to setting certain standards for how you obtain the gametes you need, and they might lead you to try to influence those who control the supply on which you depend. In a marketplace setting, the buyer does have power and you can use this positively, ensuring you can later provide your children with a sensitive view of their origins.

Each of us can consider how our influence as consumers might be used to improve conditions for those involved in the service we seek abroad. Just as parents were the main movers in getting rid of donor anonymity in the UK, we can make our preferences clear to the professionals we meet abroad to promote standards of good practice. If enough of us ask about the after-care of donors, for better donor information, and for ID-release donors, commercial interests will eventually lead to meeting consumer demands.

Thinking about the ethics around donor conception may cause discomfort. But even if you feel stirrings of guilt or blame, or if you feel judged, please don't turn away from this discussion. It may help to realise that this is a real conflict that can be resolved by careful consideration and balancing of the different pressures. In order to go ahead with creating your family, it is much better to face the issues and make your choices from a position of careful consideration, rather than turn away from the difficulties and have no answer when faced with them later. The difference is that you can explain the process by which you reached your choice, and you will be much stronger when answering your child's questions in the future.

## 9.2 Your child's rights

Your child's right to information and / or contact with their donor depends on when, where and how they were conceived, and the law that applies to that time and location. Following the Human Fertilisation and Embryology Act 1990, the Human Fertilisation and Embryology Authority (HFEA) was created in 1991 to oversee and regulate fertility treatment in the UK and provide a register of all authorised treatments, and the donors, recipients and children born thereof. A new set of regulations came into force in 2005, and a new Act was passed in 2008, which came into effect the following year.

I will look at the legislation and amendments in reverse order, starting with the most recent. In many cases, the legislation is passed (and dated) in one year, but not brought in until the following year.

October 2009
The new HFE Act 2008 stated that clinics must take account of 'the welfare of the child' and children's need for 'supportive parenting' when providing assisted conception, but will no longer have to include in this the

child's 'need for a father'. Thus, all you need to demonstrate (if asked) is how you plan to meet your children's need for supportive parenting, irrespective of the number, or gender, of parent(s).

April 2005
Amendments to the HFE Act 1991 made it compulsory for anyone donating after this date to allow the disclosure of identifying details to the child on reaching the age of 18. The revised Act invited donors to provide additional information, including a 'letter' to any child born from their donation. This information is available to parents at the time of treatment or any later stage on request, or to the children from age 18.

Additionally, parents who can show they used donated gametes can apply to the HFEA for information of any other children (number, gender and year of birth) born from the same donor, until their child reaches the age of 18.

At age 16, a donor conceived young person can get non-identifying information about their donor, and if they intend to enter an intimate (i.e. sexual) relationship, they can check if their intended partner was conceived from the same donor.

At age 18, a young person can check with the HFEA to find out whether they were conceived with donor gametes. If they were, they can get the information about any other children born from the same donor. They may register their willingness to make contact with half-siblings or with the donor if they request, and

if they were conceived after the 2005 change, they can obtain identifying information about the donor: their full name and last known address, as well their date and town of birth. The young person will be offered guidance and support if they intend to trace the donor. There are a small number of exceptions to this, as some anonymous donations made before 2005 were allowed to be used, for instance by families who already had one child, so younger siblings could have the same donor. The HFEA will be able to confirm whether this was the case for any applicant. They list all the information available on their website (1). There is no right to information about the children born into the donor's family, and the donor's family members have no right to any information from the register.

This amendment also invited those who donated prior to 2005 to offer more information, and even to allow identifying information to be disclosed to the offspring at 18. A surprising number of donors responded to this (175 in 2018, meaning a possible 1750 families), even though there was NO targeted publicity at all.

**August 1991**

The HFE Act 1990 came into force in the UK in August 1991, fuelled by fears of abuse in the research on assisted conception, genes and their manipulation. The press was fired up by the science fiction potential of IVF and other new developments, so the Act provided strict rules for the collection, storage and use of donated sperm and eggs, and a register of all treatment centres, cycles, donors, recipients and their children.

Patients and their children were given the right to basic details about their donor such as height, build, race and colouring, and some donors volunteered details such as their qualifications, job or interests. All donors were guaranteed anonymity, based on the belief that it would be impossible to recruit donors without this protection, and a fixed payment for 'expenses' was set at £15 for a sperm donation.

**Before August 1991**

Before the HFE Act 1990 came into force, there was no national legislation or regulation. There was only the general guidelines on testing and record-keeping set by professional bodies such as the Royal College of Obstetricians and Gynaecologists (RCOG). There were no centralised records. NHS services had to abide by the local rules, but private practitioners kept their own records and could destroy them whenever they wished. People born of donated sperm or eggs before this date have no right to any information about the treatment that led to their conception, or about the donor or possible half-siblings.

**Registers**

There are two registers that hold information about some donors and offspring from before the first legislation in 1990. The Donor Conceived Register (part of the National Gamete Donation Trust) (2) took over UK DonorLink in 2012. It is an independent voluntary register of ex-donors and donor-conceived people from before the introduction of the HFEA register in August 1991. It provides advice and support to match offspring from the same donor or even the donor themselves, if they are also registered. They encourage DNA testing to confirm the match. As of July 2018, they had 91 donors and 265 donor-conceived people on their register, and 99 other donor relatives (i.e. donor's family members).

The alternative is the Donor Sibling Registry (DSR) (3), set up in 2000 by Wendy Kramer and her donor-conceived son, Ryan, in Colorado, USA. This is an online register that includes many UK donor-conceived children as well as UK-based families that used imported sperm from the USA or travelled to the USA for treatment. Although the data on UK donors and offspring is limited, there are active discussion boards that can be informative and inspiring if you are interested in this area. The DSR is a charity, and charges a fee to contact anyone on the register. However, viewing the register and participating on the discussion boards is free.

**HFEA registers**

The 1990 Act and its subsequent amendments mean that donor offspring aged 16 or over now have a right to certain information, and by 2023, the first cohort of donor conceived 18 year-olds will have the right to their donor's identifying information. The HFEA is (in 2018) in the process of setting up a system for this, supported by an advice and counselling service for the offspring and the donors (4).

The Donor Sibling Link (5) is the first stage in this process: all donor offspring born under the Act who have reached 18 can register to find out about and contact any other offspring from the same donor.

**Children conceived in the UK but outside the licensed system:**

If you conceived your child outside the licensed system, for instance in a private arrangement with a known donor or with sperm provided by an online service or third party, the HFE Act and the subsequent regulations will not apply. The pros and cons of this choice are fully discussed earlier in Chapter 3. I will focus on the legal aspects here. These arrangements can provide the children with varying levels of information and / or contact. They might include contact with donor siblings and other members of the donor's family, such as grandparents, aunts and uncles, partners and children, but they are entirely at the discretion of those involved. Any agreement that was made in the planning stage will not have any legal status, so it cannot provide any guarantees against changes in feelings and interest when a real child comes into the equation.

Your child's rights in these circumstances will be the same as those conceived conventionally, with no entitlement to information or protection from the donor. The donor, even if not registered on the birth certificate, can apply for parental rights (by obtaining permission from a family court), including contact with or custody of the child. Child support and benefit agencies can demand that a known or informal donor contributes towards the child's support.

In such situations, the family court's role is always to make decisions in favour of the child's best interests, with parental interests and welfare being secondary. No prior agreement made by parents will be recognised if it is deemed to override the child's rights or best interests. At best, any agreement that you made may be seen by the court as a statement of intent at the time of writing. However, it would not have any legal weight, and would only be upheld if it was in the child's best interests. The courts take the view that the child's welfare is paramount: that a child has a right of access to both parents, and that nobody is entitled to sign away their children's rights or their duty towards their child.

The only way for a sperm donor not to acquire any legal obligations in law is to donate through the formal channels and use a clinic for the conception. In all other circumstances, the donor may be recognised as a legal parent (even against his will) and be granted parental responsibility. If you wished to claim financial support later, you will be asked for evidence of the father's identity, and if there is a name on the birth certificate, that person may have a financial obligation towards the child.

For a thorough review of the way the law has dealt with donation issues, see reference below to the 'Knowledge Centre' on Natalie Gamble's website (6).

**Children conceived abroad**

Treatment that takes place abroad is not covered by UK regulations and no information will be kept or registered in the UK. If you export sperm for treatment abroad, it will not be on the HFEA register either. The country in which you had your treatment may keep a register and have relevant legislation, so you need to find out about the local situation as regards you or your children's rights to information. Treatment here with imported gametes in a registered clinic must meet UK standards, and so the donors and children will be on the register.

## 9.3 The donor's rights and duties

**Donors within the licensed system:**

All donors who donated within the licensed system regulated by the HFE Act 1990 and subsequent legislation have certain rights and duties as well as some legal protection. This applies both to donors who are donating to a clinic or sperm bank, and to donors who are donating to someone known to them, as long as they are doing so formally through a clinic. Donors providing sperm outside of the clinic system do so without the protection of the law.

Sperm donors must provide information about their health and have a series of tests and checks to ensure they are fit to donate. This information will be registered with the HFEA. Donated sperm is kept for six months, after which the donor is rechecked to ensure there are no incubating infections that weren't picked up in the first round of test. After this, the sperm becomes available for use. The information collected will be available to the recipients and any offspring on application.

Neither the donor nor the recipient will be given the donor's HFEA registration number, as these have been classified as identifying details. Any codes or names provided by the clinic or sperm bank are supposed to be assigned in a way that does not allow comparisons between patients for informal sibling or donor tracing.

There is no duty for donors to provide updates on health issues, even though these might be important to any offspring. However, some donors do this on their own initiative. Health information is one of the main requests families tend to have as a child is growing up, either to explain issues the child is experiencing or to provide reassurance about the future.

Donors can ask the HFEA for information on the number, gender and year of birth of any offspring from their donation, but they are never entitled to any identifying information. Having donated within the licensed system, they do not have any parental rights or duties, and this would be upheld if challenged in court.

Donors who donated prior to the 2005 changes can register their willingness to be identifiable if any offspring should request this at age 18 or over. Those who donated before the HFE Act 1990 can register additional information with the Donor Conceived Register, including identifying details if they wish, for offspring who are seeking more information.

**Donors outside the licensed system:**
Donors who have operated outside the licensed system, whether it is as friends or through an intermediary such as a web-based service, do not have any of the rights or protection provided by the HFE Act. They are covered by the rest of family law, which will see them as the legal father unless a genetic link can be disproven. They could be liable to financial support and a court may order that they have a right of access and shared parental responsibility, irrespective of any agreement that may have been made between the donor and recipient beforehand.

**There is some legal precedent for this:**
Re G and Re Z (2013): Two sperm donors who were not legal fathers were given permission to make applications for contact with their biological children on the basis that they had, through previous contact, formed sufficient connection.

M v F and H (2013): The family court held a sperm donor liable for child support and substantial legal costs after finding that the donor, who had met a married woman via a donor-matching website, had donated through sexual intercourse.

In 2012 Mark Langridge was successfully pursued by the Child Support Agency for maintenance payments for two children, twelve years after donating his sperm in a private arrangement.

Donors not operating through a clinic or sperm bank have no obligation to submit to any health checks or provide any information, or to keep track of how many donations they make or how many offspring result.

## 9.4 Donor siblings

The HFEA will disclose the number of other children, their gender and year of birth, born from the donor you used. They will not provide any further detail, nor will they condone any action that might facilitate sibling tracing before the offspring reach 18. It is their legal responsibility to protect the privacy of donors, and in a situation where an egg-share donor conceived her own child with donated sperm, and also donated an egg or embryo from the same batch, there is a risk that offspring who trace their siblings would thereby trace the egg donor.

In the UK, the law limits the number of families that can be created by any donor to ten. This also applies to imported sperm, though the limit applies only to UK families. The donor's sperm might be sold in many other countries, some of which may not have any limits set by law. It is not unusual in the US for a donor to have over 100 offspring across the country.

Contact with half siblings from the same donor is a recent development and has been a positive experience for many of those involved. It is dealt with in its own right in chapter 10, and here only in terms of individual rights. Some US sperm banks have started to provide a sibling tracing register for their own customers, which UK-based users can also access.

However, as the HFEA has stated that donor registration numbers constitute identifying information and may not be released to recipients or their children, matches are not always easy to make. Name, date of birth and last known address can be given to those conceived after the 2005 changes when they are over 18, but not in other cases.

### 9.5 The rights of the extended family

When donors have donated via a clinic, nobody in their family will have any rights in regards to offspring conceived by donated gametes, although the donor can register information about his or her children, parents and other family members, including an interest in making contact. This information will be recorded on the HFEA register (if they donated after 1991) or the Donor Conceived Register (if prior to 1991) The donors of imported sperm may not know about this, although they will have agreed that their name and address at time of donation may be provided to any offspring who ask when they reach the age of 18.

The interests of family members in the case of private donation are an important issue to be considered so that plans can be put in place. There are many potential advantages – extra grandparents, aunts, uncles and cousins to provide a loosely extended family and give the child a sense of history and belonging, but also potential risks which are difficult to foresee, so it is important to think ahead and plan for the unpredictable.

If you are separated from a former spouse bear in mind that, if the marriage or civil partnership is still in place, your spouse will be the legal parent of any child conceived. This means that if you are separated from a spouse or legal partner and considering fertility treatment, it is important to consider getting a legal separation or divorce before you start trying to conceive. If you don't, an ex-partner could assert their legal right over your child, even if the relationship ended many years before.

Natalie Gamble Associates is one of the leading law firms working in the area of donor conception and offers a wealth of free information on the website, including a thorough review of the rights of the different parties (6).

## 9.6 Gametes and embryos: permissions, ownership and storage

Permissions: Although the trade in eggs, sperm and embryos is subject to the European Directive on Human Tissue and Cells Donation there are important differences between donation of gametes and blood or kidney donation. In the latter, the donation is improving or prolonging the recipient's quality of life, whereas in the former, it is creating / contributing to a life that would not exist without it. The European directive specifies that donations must be voluntary and traceable by the system, as well as other specifications on safe storage, use and movement. A patient can donate an organ to a chosen friend or relative if it is a live donation, but the choice of recipient is the medics' when it is posthumous. If we leave the EU, there is a chance that the UK will have to produce its own set of regulations to replace the European directives: at the time of writing, there is no definitive information, so do check the current situation current.

The HFEA guidance is that clinics must ask donors in the UK for what purpose their gametes may be used; they can choose multiple options from a list, which includes research and fertility treatment. They must actively consent for their gametes to be used by lesbian or gay couples and single women. They are also asked to state what should happen to their samples if they die.

> *[At my clinic] ...the number of sperm donors was limited to those (four out of a possible 12) who had given consent for use by single women. They didn't give me a proper choice of donors, which I might have had if I'd had a partner.*
>
> *Anon.*

Anecdotal evidence shows that in some cases restrictions on family type have not been made clear to people choosing a donor, meaning that in some instances they have had the distressing experience of being informed that they cannot use their chosen donor due to their family set-up.

Some clinics do not use donors who have set any restrictions, in order to ensure all their patients have the same range of choice. It may be worth asking your clinic about any restrictions before you start choosing a donor, especially if it's a smaller centre that does not advertise its openness to single women. Being single is not recognised as a characteristic that needs defending by the law, so it is legal to discriminate.

## Embryos

In several states in the USA, the term embryo adoption is used rather than donation, conferring a special status to the embryo. This has interesting consequences for the law and practice. Where the embryo is up for adoption the donor(s) may specify the sort of family they want for their embryo, select or even meet the recipient, and potential adopters have to go through a more thorough assessment than for simple sperm or egg donation. In the UK, we classify embryos as similar in nature to eggs or sperm until they have implanted, and they can be donated and received without any additional conditions or permission.

## Ownership

Technically, donated sperm and eggs remain the property of the donor until they are inseminated or transferred into the recipient's body. Donors therefore have to renew their permission for the gametes to be stored when the initial contract runs out. The length of the contract is discretionary, and sperm banks can advise on usual practice, which is anything from one to ten years. Separate consent must be obtained to store gametes for more than ten years. When a contract is coming to an end, the storage facility will contact donors to renew their permission.

This means that if someone has embryos with which they are hoping to try to conceive in future, but waits beyond the period the donors gave their permission for storage, they may be prevented from using them. In the case of double donation, both donors actively have to renew their permission. If they don't answer letters from the clinic, they are deemed to have withdrawn their permission.

In some cases, clinics have suggested an initial period of storage of three years. If an egg-share donor had a baby following the donation, she will be asked to renew the contract when her child is a toddler. If she does not respond to the letter requesting permission she will be deemed to be refusing it, and the recipient will be blocked from using any frozen embryos that she had been thinking of as hers. A sense of ownership from the recipient is not unreasonable, given that she has paid for the eggs and their storage, and may be raising a child who is a full genetic sibling to the embryos. So although she deemed any remaining embryos to be at her disposal, from a certain date it may no longer be true.

No matter how careful treatment centres are in explaining all the detail to their patients, it is not realistic for people desperate for any chance of a baby to retain these complexities, and this type of issue may come as a painful shock further down the line. It is important to be aware of the implications so you know how the length of the storage contract may affect your plan to use any additional embryos, and perhaps select a donor whose gametes are available for longer. Bear in mind also that donors can contact their facility to withdraw their permission at any time.

**Decisions about stored eggs / embryos**

Storage facilities have a duty to dispose of any sperm, egg or embryo they do not have permission to store, and so they will request renewal notification from the donor as the expiry date of the existing contract approaches. As explained, you may be paying for the storage of gametes / embryos that do not actually belong to you, so consent from the donor is still required.

If you are paying to store gametes, you will also have to renew your storage plan when it expires. There may come a point where this decision is difficult because you may no longer believe you will be using them yourself, but the thought of not having them feels too final, or none of other options seems appealing.

There are three options:

- donate the gametes to someone else needing assisted conception
- donate the gametes for research
- allow the gametes to be disposed of (your clinic may use the words 'allow (the eggs / embryos) to perish' - be prepared for this).

If you are struggling with this decision, the State of Victoria Assisted Reproduction Authority (VARTA) in Australia has devised a decision-making tool to help you weigh up the options (7). It asks you to 'score' your feelings on a variety of pros and cons, which might feel a bit mechanical, but it may help you to be clearer about all the issues and know what you need before you can decide.

## References


1. www.hfea.gov.uk/donation/donors/rules-around-releasing-donor-information/
2. donorconceivedregister.org.uk/
3. www.donorsiblingregistry.com
4. www.hfea.gov.uk/donation/donors/information-for-past-applicants/preparing-to-access-identifying-information-about-your-donor/
5. www.hfea.gov.uk/donation/donor-conceived-people-and-their-parents/donor-sibling-link-dsl/
6. www.nataliegambleassociates.co.uk/knowledge-centre
7. www.varta.org.au/resources/brochure/what-do-your-unused-embryos-decision-tool
8. Blyth, E. and Kramer, W.: My Daddy's Name is Donor': Read with caution! BioNews, *9 July 2010*

# Chapter 10: Sibling and donor tracing

*"All of our lives have been enriched by our expanded definition of family..."* Mum of two young adults who have met donor siblings through the DSR.

## 10.1 Why seek to trace donor siblings?

The bulk of this chapter looks at sibling tracing, or to be precise, the tracing of siblings born from the same donor. I will be using the term 'donor sibling' to avoid any confusion with other relationships that might warrant the term. Donor sibling tracing is less controversial and a very different enterprise to donor tracing, which is considered in section 10.8.

Many solo mums are keen to build links with other similar families so their children do not feel their origins or family structure is odd or unusual. If among those links there are families sharing the same donor, this would provide the children with relatives which most of us cannot hope to provide due to our age and circumstances. Many of us stop at having one child, either because we feel that's as much as we can manage, or because our age is making it less likely we'll succeed. If we have siblings ourselves with nieces and nephews, they are likely to be older than our own children, so not many of our kids have cousins of the same age either.

The best exploration of all aspects of sibling and donor tracing are in Wendy Kramer (1) and Rosanna Hertz (2018) (2). Wendy Kramer set up the Donor Sibling Registry (DSR) (3) in 2000, along with her son Ryan who was interested in finding out more about his donor.

Among the thousands of matches made on her website since then, there is a consistent theme of rewarding encounters that are supportive and lasting, providing an extended family and support network over the years. Of course this is not 100%, and we know little of the occasions when it turns into nothing much or even goes wrong, since the function of the website is to promote contact and those for whom it fails probably back off in silence rather than publicising it. However, the accounts of when it goes well are so simple and plausible, it has certainly convinced me that it should be available to anyone who wants to try.

For a review of the relationships within and between donor conceived families, and between them and the donors, see Ken Daniels' chapter in Kate Fine's edited collection of essays Donor Conception for Life (2015) and Rosanna Hertz's book 'Random Families' (2).

Way back when my son was tiny and I was leaving him at the crèche at one of my first DCN meetings, I noticed another toddler who looked surprisingly like him: it dawned on me that there might be an obvious reason! Of course: there could well be other children in the crèche that day born from the same donor, making them donor siblings.

Immediately I thought this would be great: my only nephew is 15 years older than my son and I would definitely not be having any more children, so this would be as near as we could get to an extended family with children his own age. I was excited by the idea that children who share the same donor may have similarities and might make good friends, and I would no doubt feel I had a lot in common with the other mum. I had always thought it would be good for my son to know other donor-conceived children, but it would be even better to develop links with donor siblings in order to widen his network of identity-affirming relationships.

Others have spoken of hopes for links in case of a future medical need, or for information that might relate to current medical issues. I think that hopes to 'insure' against the future possibility of a need for an organ donation or similar is ambitious – firstly because donor siblings are no more likely to be compatible with your child than you are, and secondly because it's not reasonable to expect the donor link to feel like a family obligation to anybody else. However if we hope to minimise the sense of oddity or isolation for our children, then it must be good to know other children who share their genetic origin as well as their mode of conception.

## 10.2 Why not?

I was surprised to come across strong reactions against the idea of sibling tracing when I first wrote about it in the DCN News in 2000 (issue 16). It forced me to recognise that it does not have the same attraction to everyone. Many families - and not just conventional two parent families - feel that they are fine as they are and have no need to extend or reach out, or even simply to find out more information about 'siblings' being raised in other families. Sometimes there is a fear that having such 'unusual' relationships might make the child feel different, or the belief that relationships with donor-siblings are no more important than are those with donors. And sometimes there is a fear that these other families might prompt negative feelings such as

jealousy or resentment in their children, either towards the other family or their own.
In solo mums' families, our 'difference' is not hidden so it's simpler for us to recognise the possible advantages of making links without fearing that it will 'out' us: we're 'out' already, so our kids may as well know they are not alone, there is nothing exceptional about their family or their origins.

There are several implications to consider before starting a search. Firstly, any activity that might lead to identifying donor siblings needs to done openly and with due care; it is in everyone's interests to avoid the disappointment of making a match and then one party pulling away when they realise they do not want the outcome.

Secondly, activities that involve gathering large numbers of donor conceived children and families together run the risk that some families will decide to exclude themselves rather than risk an accidental match. For many people, there is an optimum number beyond which they can feel overwhelmed, or the disadvantages start to outweigh the advantages.

### 10.3 The early days of sibling tracing

After that flash of insight at the door of the crèche, my mind was racing and led me to cyberspace, where I came across others who were having the same thoughts. At the time, Barry Stevens from Canada was making a film (5) about the search for his donor that led to him making contact with a host of others conceived in the same London clinic in the 1950s,some of whom turned out to be his donor-siblings. A little after this, in

2000, Wendy Kramer was setting up the Donor Sibling Registry (DSR) (3) in the USA to help her son Ryan reach out to others who, like him, were not allowed to have any information about the donors who had helped conceive them.

The result was a mountain of research and fascinating reading and learning, and the start of the SibLink Forum and Register on the DCN's website. It was only available to DCN members, and was well concealed from those who were not positively interested, but nevertheless several matches were made, and some of the young people involved have spoken up about the relationships they formed.

When the DCN's website was taken down and redesigned in 2012, the SibLink was left out, and a group of us got together to work out how we could set up something more wide-reaching and effective. After three years, we sadly had to abandon our efforts. We had developed what looked like a plausible working model and had some suggestions for the design and funding, but none of us had the time anymore to take charge of the project (6).

## 10.4 The obstacles in the UK

As it stands, the HFEA has made it virtually impossible for parents to obtain a donor number (or the Unique Identifying Code that the HFEA allocates) or information about where the donor donated (if from the UK). This is on the grounds that it might breach the donor's confidentiality, which the law states must be protected until the offspring reach the age of 18.

This is changing as more people are using sperm or eggs from overseas in treatment overseas, or with home insemination, where they *might* be given a donor code number, since this treatment is not covered by UK law. Some clinics or gamete donor banks in the UK are also now providing more detailed biographical information about the donor, making it more possible to use such information to connect with others. The bigger sperm providers in the UK are identifying their donors with numbers or codes to help their patients choose from the list, but they must ensure that these cannot be used by their clients to identify a common donor.

There is a conspiracy of silence around the fact that their descriptions can quickly be used to check if two families have a common donor, and in other cases, a donor has been identified when a client (or her mother!) has seen interviews used to recruit more donors. There is an underlying injunction that all efforts must be made to protect donor anonymity until the offspring can make their formal request at age 18, and this includes the identifying of donor siblings. One reason for this is the fact that some donors are also recipients, for instance women who have donated eggs or embryos on an egg-share scheme, may have used donor sperm: many of those who donate their eggs are younger lesbian couples. Identifying their own children's donor-siblings will identify them as the egg-donor.

One common fear for parents is that a donor might identify their offspring and make contact that would threaten the child's security. There is a risk that the recipient is successful in her treatment, but the donor is not. It is a convoluted and confusing situation, but it's best to recognise this before getting too far into the process of searching.

Until recently, in many cases people had little information about the donor and often assumed (mistakenly) that the donation was made at the clinic where they (or their parents) were treated. The DSR in the USA arranges its data according to the name of the sperm or egg bank that was used and the donor number / code, the two details that we in the UK are usually missing. Of course, anyone who has imported sperm or eggs from the USA, or from one of the Scandinavian sperm banks that also export to the USA, should have sufficient details to make it worthwhile registering on the DSR, where they have a chance of finding a match.

## 10.5 Double / embryo donation: additional complexity

There are issues that arise with double and embryo donation that may not be fully explored at the time of conception but can add complexity when considering sibling tracing later on.

Some of this is related to the fact that embryos from the same batch or produced on an egg-sharing scheme may have been used by an initial recipient who therefore has full siblings to your child. If for instance the embryo was created from a woman's egg and donated sperm, and then donated because she had either completed her own family or withdrawn from treatment for another reason, any success in tracing your child's donor siblings would also lead to you tracing the egg donor. This would be in breach of the Act's intentions, which promises anonymity to donors for 18 years, and is the reason why clinics in the UK steer clear of involvement in sibling tracing. On the other hand, if the gametes you used came from two donors unknown to each other, they might be in different countries. Each may have a child / children of their own as well as those born through their donations. The practical complexities increase, and the chance of tracing somebody may increase, even if it is not the relative that was actually sought.

## 10.6 Background to provision of donor information in the UK

Any attempt to link up with donor-siblings depends on being able to confirm that the same donor was involved, by matching their description, their donor number / code and / or by DNA testing.

Britain has an interesting history when it comes to allowing the recipients information about the gametes' origins. The first recorded example of donor insemination was performed on an anaesthetised woman with the patient's husband's consent, but not her own (7). The fear of public outrage and the judgement of the church led to secrecy shrouding the practice of donor insemination late into the 20th century. Full records were not routinely kept until mandated by the 1990 law, and clinics, both private and NHS-based, were secretive about who they recruited as donors.

In some cases, it has come to light that the doctors themselves, or their husbands or students were the sperm donors. Whether it was because infertile men would want absolute secrecy, or the doctors providing the sperm did not want public exposure, there was no regard for the needs of the children, or for the risks of the practice being carried out without any scrutiny or agreed standards. As is often the case, they claimed they were doing this for the patient's own good. This may have been entirely sincere, but it did not match with the evidence that was coming out of studies of adoption, or with the general trend for medical practice to become more open and involve informed consent.

Couples who went for donor insemination were generally reassured that the sperm came from fit and healthy men, sometimes with an attempt to match the husband's physical characteristics in order for the child to resemble its father. There was little choice if any, the decision was made by the doctors, and donors were guaranteed absolute anonymity. The patients were sometimes advised to have intercourse when they got home, so that they could believe there was a chance the husband was the biological father. They were usually advised to tell nobody and all would be fine. In some cases, they were told that the sperm was mixed from two different donors in order to ensure that nobody could be identified.

When reproductive medicine started to become a more lucrative and prestigious industry in the 1970s, it became clear that controls and standards were needed. Following a period of voluntary regulation, the HFE Act 1990 led to the establishment of a statutory body, the HFEA, which now regulates, inspects and monitors all fertility treatment in the UK.

At this stage, donors had to provide medical histories and sketchy personal details, but there was no instruction as to how much information the patients should get, either before or after treatment. In some clinics, staff were still selecting the donor, sometimes with an option for the patients to state what features they would prefer. In other centres, patients might have details of a few donors from whom they could chose, usually just basic physical characteristics. Some clinics would routinely send donor information out when a pregnancy was confirmed, others might wait until asked, and some would refuse, claiming that this was not allowed.

Two issues underlie this situation:

- a resistance to anything that might look like allowing people to 'design' their baby, fearing this smacks of eugenics, and
- an unquestioned belief that doctors had a right to make these decisions for people, and a culture that granted them this status.

Meanwhile in the USA the fertility industry developed as a free market. Sperm banks were generally independent of treatment centres. They published catalogues where the patients could choose their ideal donor and order their sperm in batches for the future. By the mid-1990s, some in the UK realised that there was nothing to stop them shopping for their sperm in the USA and importing it, if they wanted more choice and information than available here.

At the same time, the stigma surrounding infertility and the use of donor-assisted treatment was gradually waning (although some stigma remains to this day) and more parents felt duty-bound to be open with their children about their origins. The realisation that children might want or need more information, even the donor's identity, was growing. This culminated in the changes introduced in the UK in 2005, ending donor anonymity among other things. Since then, donors (and clinics) provide more information and must agree that identifying details will be disclosed to the offspring when they reach the age of 18.

Despite the dire warnings from many doctors and the closure of several sperm banks, the supply of donors did not dry up. There was, at least initially, a change in the profile of sperm donors towards more of them being older and already having had children. Many donors are now older than the stereotype 'student in need of beer money' - often men who have some personal awareness of the distress of infertility. Sperm donation in the UK has become more altruistic and less driven by financial need, although that is far from the full story. In the case of imported sperm, which is supposed to meet UK standards, it is difficult to ensure there is no financial incentive.

From the point of view of our children, a shift towards altruism must be a good thing, since it takes out the incentive to hide possible health problems in the family and inflate their 'saleability' (and fee) by exaggerating their education and other achievements.

Due to the time taken and intrusiveness of egg donation, it has always been driven mainly by altruistic motives in the UK, as the financial compensation is not enough to be an incentive.

That is different in the case of the egg-share schemes, which provide a good proportion of the eggs donated in the UK. In this situation, a woman under 35 who needs fertility treatment but has a good supply of eggs can get discounted or even free treatment in exchange for donating some of her eggs to another woman. For many younger women who need private treatment this is a significant financial incentive. In view of the fact that these are all women who are seeking assisted reproduction, we can assume there is also an element of compassion, and thereby altruism, in the donation.

A few donor recruiting centres have redesigned their recruiting methods with some success, though there is never the choice you get in the USA. Some clinics now don't have a waiting list for donor insemination, and waiting time for egg donation treatment can be just weeks in clinics where they offer egg-sharing. Other clinics haven't changed their recruitment practices and have longer waiting lists, or they have given up trying to provide any sperm or eggs themselves and developed links with overseas suppliers and clinics. For commercial reasons, these clinics do not routinely tell patients that they could get sperm without a waiting list at a different clinic nearby.

There is still some resistance to 'sperm shopping' in the UK, but this is being eroded by the ease of access to the more open and upfront USA and Scandinavian markets. UK sperm banks are beginning to provide longer donor profiles and are allowing their patients the full range to choose from. The country's biggest sperm bank provides a website where donors' details can be viewed and compared online. A video used to recruit new donors allowed one woman to identify the donor she had used, as he provided enough detail to be recognised and traced.

Since Wendy and Ryan Kramer in Colorado set up the DSR in 2000, it has become a thriving forum for information sharing, developing our understanding and contributing to policy making. This is fully explored in section 10.9 below.

The HFE Act 1990 set up the register which records the details of every person who donated sperm, eggs or embryos for use in UK treatments since 1991, as well as any event in which they were used. Whether the donation took place in the UK or overseas, it has to meet UK standards if used in treatment here. However, the unique donor number / code that they allocate is not provided to the clinics and sperm banks, which have been allowed to develop their own coding practice. Thus some clinics would provide donor numbers in with the details they provided to their patients, and others not. It emerged that some clinics used systems such as initials and dates of birth to code their donors, thus threatening their anonymity, and eventually in 2009, the HFEA's legal advisers concluded that all donor codes were 'identifying information' and may not be given to parents or offspring.

Both prior to and since the passing of the HFE Act 1990, some donors in the UK donated at more than one sperm bank or treatment centre. Thus their details may have been recorded in different formats according to local protocols, so the information about the same donor might not always look identical. This is also true of some donors in the USA: the same donor may have a different number depending on where his sperm was bought / sold.

It is therefore difficult for those of us who used UK sperm, eggs or embryos to have information that can be matched with certainty to anyone else's. It helps if we use the exact same wording as the clinic or HFEA has provided, assuming that they are handing out the same details unedited to everyone who enquires. Ultimately, we have to rely on confirmation by DNA tests, which is also not always 100% accurate. I won't go into the science behind this here, but if you want to understand it fully, check out the leaflets on DNA, X and Y chromosome testing published by the Donor Conceived Register (DCR) (8).

### 10.7 How to start tracing

Obtaining your information from the HFEA if you were treated in the UK after August 1991: *(Please check the current situation with HFEA before you go ahead).* If your child was conceived with donated gametes in a UK licensed centre after 1 August 1991, the donor's details will be on the HFEA Register. If your child is still under 18, you can contact their Information Team (9). They will tell you what documents they need in order to provide you with all the available information about the donor, as well as the number, gender and year of birth of any other children born from the same donor.

Consider the possible outcomes and what you want / what your limits might be. If you want to maximise the chance of making a match while your child is still under 18, you may have to try one of the voluntary registries such as DSR or those run by individual sperm banks/ providers. You can check the Register to see if you can find a match, but you will improve your chances considerably if you register your own details where others can find them. Many more people browse the registries than actually register, so you may be missing out if you don't post yourself.

If you are unsure how much contact you want, be very clear about this so as not to raise anyone's hopes unfairly; much better to be cautious and then let down your barriers when you feel safe. If you use an anonymous email address, you can state that you want only anonymous contact initially. Think about whether you want to see photos of the other children, which might mean you need to be willing to share your own children's photos. You might feel safer if you make it clear that it will be baby pictures only, at least to start with.

Register / check the registers... and be patient. Ryan Kramer, who set up the DSR with his mother in the USA, had to wait 8 years to connect with any donor siblings.

### 10.8 DNA testing

This is now an integral part of the tracing process to confirm a match, as well as a first step. The popularity of genealogical research has led to a number of online commercial DNA testing services that provide information on cultural and geographical ancestry as well as links to individuals who share genetic links. Most people in the USA have backgrounds that spread to other continents, and donors in other countries often have familial links in the USA.

To choose the most appropriate DNA testing service, consider one that is in the country from which you obtained the gametes. Services based in the USA are used to working online, as are UK services. Wherever your donor may have had roots, there are likely to be family members settled in the USA whose descendants may have used DNA to trace their own background, so your enquiries might link up. Consider the size of their database - the bigger it is, the more chance of a link, and the number of regions they claim to cover. Choose between a cheek swab and a saliva (spit) test. Read up on the meaning of mitochondrial DNA so you understand the limitations of only being able to provide the maternal DNA to accompany your child's – too complicated for me to do justice here! But the main message when dealing with DNA testing services is the risk of uncovering links that you were not expecting, that lead you to question relationships you were not considering. There have been instances of people discovering one of their parents was donor conceived, as well as that a father, brother or son was a donor.

The wide range of DNA testing services has clearly made any promise of anonymity to donors a myth. They may be the best means in the future for donor conceived people to link with each other as well as the donors and their social families. However they do not yet include as standard the support and counselling services needed to help people navigate the variety of outcomes and surprises that can occur.

Wikipedia has a thorough review of all the issues and services available (10). There is a full page on 'Getting ready for contact' specially written for donor conceived people in the UK (11).

### 10.9 Sibling tracing registries

The DCN hosted a SibLink Registry that was omitted in the 2014 upgrade of the DCN website. There exists a blueprint for a more effective version, but at this stage

(January 2019) nobody has come forward to set it up and manage it (12).

**Donor Sibling Registry (DSR), USA**
This is by far the biggest registry in the world with 60,000 registrants (July 2018) from 105 countries. It is a fascinating website with thriving message boards where all sorts of relevant issues are discussed and explored. The DSR is free to browse, but charges a membership fee to enter your details or to contact someone on the register. It includes reference to the many studies to which Wendy and her organisation have contributed together with the TV programmes, films and videos for which interviewees have been provided.

Your use of the DSR may differ according to where your child was conceived, as follows:

Conceived with USA gametes: if the donated gametes you used originated in the USA, the DSR is your best forum to seek a match. You register your child's details under the name of the sperm bank. Several thousand donor-conceived people are registered, and most of them have a donor number that provides a degree of certainty, although it may miss out when a donor has donated to more than one bank, as he will be listed with different donor numbers.

Conceived in the UK: If the sperm you used was imported from the USA, then you should be able to obtain the US donor number and register your details on the DSR under the sperm bank that provided it, which is the likeliest place other recipients look. Most entries for those who have used sperm of UK origin are listed under the fertility clinic as patients didn't usually have details of the sperm bank until recently. In my view, it is better for people to list under HFEA unless they know the origin of the sperm, on the basis that each donor's samples may have been sent out to many different clinics, and each clinic will be using sperm from a number of providers. Since all sperm used in UK clinics must be registered with the HFEA, using the HFEA section of the DSR will promote your chance of connecting with others.

Conceived elsewhere: There are clinics on all continents except Antarctica (as my pedantic teenager made me include) listed on the DSR. Again, consider whether people are registering the clinic where the fertility treatment happened or where the gametes were donated.

**Donor Conceived Register (DCR), UK**

In the UK, the government-funded voluntary DCR is for adult donor offspring, donors and the non donor-conceived adult children of donors. However it is only open for conceptions that took place in the UK prior to 1 August 1991 after which time the HFEA register is the place to go. The DCR uses a DNA database as the route for establishing 'links'. It took over from UK Donor Link (UKDL) in April 2013. Funding has recently been renewed, but it is still insecure in the long term.

**HFEA Donor Sibling Link (DSL)**

The HFEA have set up a voluntary register called DSL on which anyone conceived since 1 August 1991 can register at age 18. They can specify whether they want to receive information about any other person conceived from the same donor, to let others know of their existence, or for a meeting to be facilitated. In August 2018 there are 177 donor-conceived registrants (aged 18 or over).

In 2023, the HFEA will commission a new service to manage enquiries from donor conceived 18 year-olds, providing identifying information about donors and supporting them if they want to search. At this stage, this is being referred to as Opening the Register (OTR) (13).

### 10.10 For those having treatment abroad or outside the licensed system

If your child was conceived outside the clinic system in the UK, or in a country without any donor registration, the situation is confusing and there are inconsistencies, many of which may never be disentangled. The best bet will be to use the big genealogy focussed services, which will point you in the right direction for further enquiries. It is also important to check regularly with the services you used just in case local practice changes, or the clinic receives more information they can share.

In the case of informal channels, if you did not set up any effective way of getting in touch, you will have to use the DNA testing services – see above.

### 10.11 Donor tracing

All children born since the law changed in 2005 will be able to obtain identifying information about their donors when they reach the age of 18. Many families are happy to wait until their children have grown up to do any searching, out of concern that it might be easier for the boundary between parent and donor to be blurred while the offspring are still dependent on their (social) parents. On the whole, parents' main interest in meeting the donor is usually to do with medical issues rather than wanting to know them personally. Many parents have explained this to their children in terms such as 'When you're 18, you can find the donor', implying that they will be able to trace and meet them in person.

This is misleading, as it omits several facts:

- The information that is available may only be details provided at the time of donation, as there is no duty on donors to keep the HFEA updated – so in the 18 plus intervening years, they may have moved abroad, changed name or even died.
- Although donors had to agree for their identifying details to be disclosed to 18 year- olds, they were not agreeing to any particular kind of contact, or to meet them in person. Some donors may be receptive to contact, but others may not.
- Some donors may not have told significant people such as spouse, children or parents about their history of donating gametes, maybe because it simply did not seem important anymore. They may be wary of how this might affect their parents, partners, or children and may want to avoid the risk of disclosure.

The degree of preparation and counselling for donors on this has varied widely, so some donors will have signed the consent form without any discussion of the long-term implications. Others may have recognised the implications but see them very differently when the time approaches that they might be traced and contacted.

Although donors in the UK are no longer guaranteed anonymity, this only applies to the offspring who have reached the age of 18. There may be reasons to seek a link before then.

**Why defend anonymity?**

There are three reasons why we might consider that the donor's anonymity for the first 18 years should be protected:

- Reciprocity – if we don't want to be traced by the donors while our children are growing up, we should respect donors' privacy in rerurn.
- It may discourage recruitment of new donors if it became know that their identity couldnot be protected.
- Legal – we accepted the donation on the basis the donor would be anonymous for 18 years so we should honour this 'contract'.

**Why challenge anonymity?**

There may be good reasons to trace a donor before the first offspring reaches the age of 18. This is might be a medical issue: if your child is affected by a genetic feature and you want to alert the authorities:

- to let other families that have used the same donor know
- to suspend further donations to protect others, or
- the donors themselves may be unaware of the issue and need to know.

In principle, in this situation, the HFEA should take responsibility to follow up as they have access to all the necessary information to contact all parties without delay.

We might feel pressured to try to trace a donor for a child who gets very insistent. In this case, it's important to consider the consequences and listen carefully to what your child wants / needs. If your child wants to find a 'daddy', you need to address this and rule out any hope that the donor might take this role. It's hard to deny our children their wishes, but there are impossible hopes and we won't do them any favours letting them think that all wishes are achievable – much kinder to help them identify the borderline between fairy tales and reality, and how to achieve the nearest realistic equivalent. In many cases, younger children can get fixed on something that turns out to be a fleeting interest, and we need to recognise this and treat it as it deserves: a real desire, but not a realistic one. We need to help our children learn to live with a degree of uncertainty. This is not the only area of life that presents the same dilemma and they will be more resilient if they can bear it, perhaps see it as a mystery, interesting but not worth agonising over as there is no resolution.

**Tracing ID-release donors**

Once your child is 18, or at 16 they are in an intimate relationship and need to check their partner is not related, they can contact the HFEA for the information. They will have to satisfy the requirements to prove they were conceived from licensed treatment in the UK and be offered counselling from a recognised specialist. If they say they want contact, the HFEA will try to trace the donor. Although there is no obligation for donors to update the HFEA if they move or change name, it may take time and ultimately be unsuccessful – for instance if the donor has died or left the country.

If found, they will tell the donor that one of their offspring is interested in contact, and if the donor agrees, both parties will be referred to an intermediary agency to facilitate a meeting. If they wish, your child can go ahead with the information from the registry (name, date of birth and address at the time of donation) to track down and contact the donor themselves.

There are various unpredictable elements, such as whether the donor has a partner and family who may not know of the existence of donor siblings, or the donor turns out to be quite different to what they'd imagined, and not in a positive way. Donors are not obliged to tell their own family and may be defensive, at least to start. It is best to be prepared for various outcomes by having considered some of the risks and how to handle them, maybe by contact with a professional or a peer group such as on the DSR. One factor that is particular to children of one-parent families is that the donor may fear our kids have a higher expectation of them, either emotionally or materially, imagining that our children have grown up 'deprived'. It might help to address these possible fears before planning any contact or meeting.

Wendy Kramer now has 18 years' experience of helping people make connection with donor siblings and donors, and her book covers many aspects and possible outcomes. Her organisation has generated online forums (14) that are excellent places to sound out others and share thoughts and experiences. More of the bigger sperm banks (e.g. Xytex and California Cryobank in the US, European Sperm Bank and Cryos in Denmark) are setting up their own systems for enquiries about ID-release donors / donor siblings, but it's worth noting that many of their clients will be registering with the DSR for a better chance of making connections. It may well be that as the 2023 timeline approaches, similar structures develop here for UK conceived people: the DCN or the HFEA should be able to point you in the right direction.

## References


1. Kramer, W. and Cahn, N.: Finding our Families, Penguin Random House, 2013
2. Hertz, R. and Nelson, M.: Random Families: Genetic Strangers, Sperm donor Siblings and the Creation of New Kin, Oxford UP, 2018
3. www.donorsiblingregistry.com/
4. Daniels, K.: Understanding and Managing Relationship in Donor Assisted Families in Fine, K. (ed): Donor Conception for Life, Karnac, 2015
5. Stevens, B.: Offspring, documentary, 1997: https://vimeo.com/128603400
6. DCN journal articles about sibling tracing:
   DCN Journal Summer 2010, Issue 2: p.1-9
   DCN Journal Summer 2017, Issue 16: p.6
7. www.huffpost.com/entry/a-brief-history-of- donor-conception_b_9814184
8. donorconceivedregister.org.uk/dna/
9. https://www.hfea.gov.uk/i-am/donor-conceived-people-and-their-parents/
10. https://isogg.org/wiki/DNA_testing_for_the_donor conceived
11. https://isogg.org/wiki/Information_for_donor-conceived_people:_getting_ready_for_contact
12. www.hfea.gov.uk/about-us/news-and-press-releases/2018-news-and-press-releases/hfea-statement-on-donor-conceived-register
13. https://ifqlive.blob.core.windows.net/umbraco-website/1480/opening-the-register-report.pdf
14. www.facebook.com/pages/biz/non_profit/Donor-Sibling-Registry-Connecting-Donor-Families-1460854104145782/

## Chapter 11: Contingency planning for solo mums

In memory of Kate.

*"Thinking about the worst-case scenario is no more likely to make it happen than thinking about sex can make you pregnant!"* Emily's aphorism...

### 11.1 What to plan for and why?

This chapter deals with issues most of us would prefer to ignore but that we really need to prioritise in a way that is not as critical for two-parent families and people without dependents, since we do not have a second parent to do it in the moment. We owe it to our children to do the objective thinking beforehand and make provisions so crises are less traumatic. If it is difficult to read this chapter, take it step by step and start with the least threatening, but do not turn your back on it. At every stage, you can be proud that you are facing the most difficult outcomes and protecting your child, and hope that none of it will ever be needed!

To have chosen or be deciding to start a family on your own is a hugely confident and optimistic decision, and none of us wants to be reminded of the risk of accidents, illness or other emergencies, times when our children might need someone to step in because we are incapacitated, even for the briefest moment. I expect that most solo mums are good planners, having had to weigh up their circumstances to make the decision and then work their way through the treatment minefield. In my case, as for many of us I expect, once I had my baby in my arms, I sighed with the biggest relief and settled into my new life, and fleeting thoughts of disaster were pushed out of mind as fast as they surfaced.

Much as we may like to believe 'it won't happen to me', it is important to realise that we are all vulnerable. I have had the privilege to get to know many other solo mums. Sadly, some years back our friend Kate succumbed to the cancer she had been living with for years. Her ten-year-old donor-conceived daughter remained safely at home with her grandmother, her aunt and uncle sharing her care. This sad situation spurred me on to writing this chapter, so thank you Kate.

For readers who have not yet assigned guardians or made a will, please take this opportunity to move forward and take action, and if you haven't even thought about this yet, please read and consider what plans you need to put in place.

> *After I had it all written up (...) I felt myself relax and stopped imagining awful events happening to my daughter and no one there to specifically look after her. In fact I had not realised how this worry had impacted on my everyday thoughts.*
>
> *Nicky B., mum to two*

Two of the women who responded to the survey of solo mums mentioned that their clinic required a named guardian before they could begin treatment: they had to confront this prospect even before being a parent. It may have felt discriminatory at the time, but on another level, it is not such a bad policy. The adoption process will also require you to identify fall-back resources if things should go wrong. Planning for the worst may feel pessimistic, but it cannot do any harm, and it could make a huge difference should anything go wrong.

Of course, plans don't only need to be in place in case you die, the most mundane things can happen – a sprained ankle, a dose of flu, a stomach bug or a crisis with another family member can put you in a situation where it's hard to prioritise the stability and security your child needs. Forward planning could save a lot of stress and legwork in a crisis, and defuse the anxieties we push to the back of our mind. The event for which you need to prepare could in fact be a more positive one such as the imminent arrival of your second baby, although you usually have plenty of time to prepare, all sorts of things can happen that put you out of action at short notice.

## 11.2 Paving the way

Caring for a growing child is a complex and ever changing responsibility. Families are more scattered and smaller than they used to be, and the friendship networks we built up as single working women are less likely to fit with the lifestyle of a new mum. Many of us find that we make friends among other new mums and neighbours - building a village is discussed in earlier chapters. Childcare, whether nanny, nursery or childminder, will require contact details for back-up carers, in case they cannot get hold of you in an emergency. I was not prepared for this and was thrown into a panic, so I gave my sister's details. Although she was perfectly willing to take on this role, she lives a good hour away, which would have made it almost useless in practice. I soon arranged with another single mum who lived nearby to back each other up, which lasted for years as our kids later went to nursery and school together.

This kind of mutual set-up is ideal. If it works out, it can cover a variety of situations. Our children were probably the youngest in the area to start having sleepovers, as we got into the habit of giving each other a night off for birthdays and other occasions, as well as daytime care for hairdressing, dentist appointments and the like. We invested in a second-hand double buggy between us, which was a fantastic resource for a few years. Although our paths would not have crossed in my previous life, she was utterly trustworthy and we grew to love each other's children. We learnt a lot from each other, as well as providing great moral support.

My experience was that other single mothers were freer to help and more flexible than those with partners, and more available evenings and weekends, but you may find things are different. I found that other single parents appreciated the reciprocity, so it tended to work better as there was give and take in the relationship.

### 11.3 Emergency measures

Whatever your situation, you will most likely need someone to look after your child at some stage, maybe without the opportunity to plan ahead. This could be because you have an accident, a family emergency, or simply an appointment to which you cannot take your child. There may be family nearby to step in, but it is a good idea to have alternative options for such eventualities.

Your need for emergency care may be short term, such as a few hours until you sort out a crisis, or longer term if you get sick or have an accident and cannot look after your child on your own for a while. Any mutual or casual back-up arrangements you have in place should be able to cover most short-term problems. This would take the sting out of a crisis and give you time to work out longer-term needs and solutions.

In all situations, try to ensure your child experiences as little disruption as possible.

- Being looked after by people whom they know is preferable to strangers, even if those strangers are trained and qualified.
- It is not always possible, but if your child can stay at home, with familiar toys and bed, that will be less disruptive than going to stay somewhere unfamiliar.
- However, if your child is already used to staying with certain friends, this may make things easier.

How children react to these sorts of situations will also vary with age and personality.

Friends and Family

It can be helpful to think in advance how you would deal with various situations. If you got sick, would there be someone who might be able to stay with you to help out? Could they support you so you can continue to be there for your child, while they take on the tasks you are unable to manage? Do you know a student or young person who might be keen to get away from home and help for a few days?

Alternatively, is there somewhere both of you can go and stay until you are well enough to manage alone? Family is the obvious choice, but other friends with a spare room might be happy to have you for a while.

Alternatively, there might be a friend who could have your child overnight or during the day, depending which you can manage best. In this case, you would need to consider how to get back and forth or who could pick up / drop off your child.

Finally, an option would be for your child to go and stay somewhere they can be looked after until you are well enough to take charge again. If this is the solution, you need to ensure that you stay in contact as much as possible. Video calling, facetime or skype are great ways to connect, especially if you have done it before and it has positive associations. Seeing and hearing you can make all the difference for younger children. You can ask whoever is looking after them to help them photograph and email drawings to you, or record a song on your voicemail, for example, so that they feel they have a bit of control, and then make sure you acknowledge whatever they sent!

Just make sure that however ill you are, you remember to ask your child about how they are doing, ask them to report back to you on everyday things, make sure they know you will be back in your role as soon as you can.

Paid professional carers

If you have a babysitter, childminder or nanny who could help, this is ideal as they will already be known to your child. There are many agencies that provide trained childcare workers and nannies with enhanced DBS checks (previously known as the Criminal Records Bureau) at short notice, but it comes at a price. If you are able to prepare in advance, interview more than one so that you get a choice, and hire them for a couple of short sessions so you and your child can get to know and trust them and they can familiarise themselves with your child's habits and expectations.

Help from social services
For longer-term support if you do not have anyone who can help and cannot afford to hire help, then you can contact your local authority's family services, who have a duty to support parents and protect children. Their first response will be to help you find a solution within your own networks, but if there is no resource, they may be able to offer some support from the fostering service, or find a registered childminder who can provide temporary care in their home. Using fostering services would involve having your child officially 'looked after' by the local authority, a cumbersome bureaucratic process. However, be reassured that this process will include an 'exit strategy' from the very beginning, which should allay any fears that you wouldn't get your child back as soon as you were fit.

### 11.4 Convalescence

When you have been incapacitated, it is important to give yourself the best chance of recovery, to make sure that you are back to full health and do not relapse. This is one of those times when we need to remember our own needs, because if we neglect them, we may not be able to look after our children's needs as well as we'd like – remember all those airline instructions to fit your own oxygen mask and life jacket before your child's?

The term convalescence has gone out of fashion and it is no longer considered a service to be provided by the NHS, so it is up to each of us to find our own resources, again. You could see it as an opportunity to visit friends or relatives, or to invite someone to stay a while, so long as they are the sort who will not expect you to provide a busy or luxury break – early nights and takeaways rather than outings and gourmet home cooking!

There are many simple ways you can look after yourself – it might be treating yourself to a pyjama day, staying in, quiet one-to-one activities with your children, sorting out the photo albums, making Christmas decorations / birthday presents, doing that mending that's been waiting an age or learning some new skill... Try to organise for someone else to take your child out for a few hours of energetic play to use up their stamina and bring them back tired out!

Illness and the need for convalesce are outside of our control. All normal rules go out the window, and it is not the time to prove you can 'do it all'. The risks are too great. When it is over and you look back, that is the time to recognise you are a hero, and the heroism was your ability to put your usual independence aside for the sake of your children.

If you want to plan for your children's care, you can apply to a court for a child arrangement order – for instance, if you are facing a hospital admission in the future. This can cover where your child would live / how long for, and who would be responsible for them.

It can include more than one other caregiver. Again, the Children and Families Court Advisory and Support Service (CAFCASS) (1) is the best place to find out how you can use a child arrangement order and how to get one.

### 11.5 Making a will, power of attorney, appointing a guardian, and living wills

Once you have faced planning for emergencies, it should be easier to think of the unimaginable and make plans for a situation where your child might need someone to look after them long term. This should bring you peace of mind, as well as giving you the opportunity to prepare the ground and make sure your preferences and wishes are known. Appointing a guardian can be done verbally, but to ensure that it is recognised as your wish in the case of any dispute, it is best done formally, for instance in a will or power of attorney in case anyone disputes it when you're not able to assert your wishes.

Think of whom you would like and trust to bring up your child if you were not around, and sound out their willingness before you make any decision. Consider their parenting style, their circumstances and their flexibility. It is important to recognise that your child's needs will change over time: when they are older, for instance, it may be harder for them to change school and move away from friends. Your chosen guardian's situation may also change, for example if they have children of their own or develop health problems. Make sure that everyone knows that the plans can be adjusted over time.

> *I found this really hard. First of all I had to get over the fact that every time I thought about my son being on his own I burst into tears…*
>
> *Sue, mum to a wonderful son (age 15)*

You can assign 'back-up' guardians, in case the main guardian is unable to fulfil their duty for whatever reason. If you have areas of doubt, for instance about parenting styles, try to discuss them and find a compromise. For instance, it might not be reasonable to expect another family to get rid of their TV if your children are staying, but they might agree not to allow TV or playstations in the bedroom. If your children have always had an organic and / or vegetarian diet, you could ask for certain specifics, for instance their favourite foods to be served regularly. The more you have discussed your parenting practice and style, the more you will be able to identify how to promote consistency and minimise the risk of your children suffering a culture shock as well as their loss when the guardianship comes into practice.

Many people choose relatives as guardians, but some choose friends. If you have chosen a non-relative but have not made this formal through a will or similar, the arrangement would be classified as private fostering, and would be registered with social services and liable to visits to ensure all is going well. A court would normally grant a residence order in this situation. Their priority is to make the least possible intervention to maintain the child's welfare.

The CAFCASS website (1) is a useful source of further information and links to local specialist advisers.

*This is one of the hardest things I have ever had to do. It cost me many a tearful night ending in the assertion 'Well, I will just not have to die then!*

*Victoria T.*

**Making a will**

Wills are not only for the rich, as is often believed.
If you die without a will there is a real risk that your dependants might lose the right to inherit your property, and an even more worrying risk that they could end up in a custody dispute. You may well meet someone in the future, and if you have a surviving partner, or children from different relationships, this can become especially difficult.

It can get very complex, for instance, if you have ever been married, or if an ex-partner's children have some right over the home you shared, so make sure that you get proper advice to ensure that your estate is not used up to pay lawyers to argue it out after you've gone. If you have a surviving spouse and your estate is worth more than £250,000 but you leave no will, your children will only be entitled to only a share of the excess no matter how long you have been separated.

Some lawyers are specialists in assisting with wills, but it is by no means necessary to use a lawyer to make a valid will. There are many good guides available in public libraries, such as the one published by the consumer association Which? There is also an annual Will Aid month (which varies according to the regions), where many solicitors sign up for a scheme to provide free wills in exchange for a donation to a Will Aid charity of your choice. Many charities have their own advisers to help you write a will in return for a legacy. The firms involved often have a limited number of appointments available on the scheme, so it is worth booking early to get an appointment.

Many of the big charities also have arrangements with local law firms to help with wills for a set donation, usually much lower than the standard fee. Charities such as Oxfam run their own schemes all year round. In general, these schemes only provide for simple wills. If there is any complexity such as a spouse or ex-partner, or you own a company or a property abroad, you will need to pay for advice.

Many people think of their will as being where they record their wishes for a funeral and what happens after they die, but the will may not be referred to until the most immediate matters have been taken care of, especially if it's lodged with a solicitor who will charge for every action. It is a good idea, therefore, to record your wishes somewhere that is immediately accessible, and to let your nearest and dearest know where this is! This will include your wishes for your children's care, your funeral, the care of any pets and so on.

Bear in mind that once you have lodged your will with a lawyer (which is a convention, not a necessity), they will charge you for any changes you want to make. It is a good idea to limit the content of the will to the concrete details that are least likely to change, and to include a reference to a 'Letter of Instruction for the Executor', which you can change as circumstances require. For instance, state that you have nominated a guardian in the letter rather than naming them in the will. The Letter of Instruction would be the best place to record any specifications you might have over your children's care (and pets!), as these can change with time. This might cover educational preferences, keeping in touch with significant others, access to information about origins etc.

**Power of attorney**

This is the power you can grant to others to make

decisions on your behalf, and on which you can record your choices for when you are no longer able to express them yourself. It lapses when you die, so does not replace or supersede a will, but it is a legal document, so your wishes as stated by your attorney must be respected.

> *When my mother was descending into dementia, my sister and I had to take on power of attorney to manage her and her affairs. I realised then that it was something I ought to do too, in case I went the same way. At that stage, I named my sister as my attorney, but now that my son's eighteen, I've transferred the financial rights to him, and made them jointly responsible for decisions about care, which I think are more difficult and distressing.*
>
> *Ellie, mum to Tom, London*

There are two types of power of attorney, one for property and finances and the other for health and welfare decisions. You can have more than one attorney, and different attorneys for the different categories of decision. The power of attorney comes into effect either when you lose mental capacity to make your own decisions, which is a medical decision, or temporarily, if you so choose – for instance while you are away from home or just don't feel well enough.

The documents and regulations are available online, and the office of the public guardian (2) gives support over the phone to help you complete your application, although lawyers also offer this help at a fee. Power of attorney orders cost £82 each (at time of writing), but reductions and exemptions may apply. The documents give space for you to provide specifications, such as where you want to be looked after, and by whom, where you want your children to live, go to school, and other such preferences. An attorney must be eighteen or over, so your children can become your attorneys when they reach this age or whenever you feel they are ready. They can be completed online or downloaded, but the forms are different so take care you have the correct ones for the task (3).

It is important that your nearest and dearest know that you have a will and / or have granted a power of attorney, and where to find the documents. The time they need them will probably be a time when you are not able to tell them where to find them. It may be useful to let your GP or hospital consultant know too, as they might be involved at the relevant time. Another useful tip is to use the facility to leave information on your mobile phone in a file called ICE (In Case of Emergency), which can be accessed without your pin number. Emergency services are familiar with this and will check if there is a next of kin or other emergency information.

Finally, to complete the portfolio of legal planning documents, you might consider a living will. This could include an advance care plan, about how and where you want to be looked after, and an advance directive, a document co-signed and kept by your doctor or consultant, to ensure they know your wishes, including what treatment you would prefer not to have if you have lost your capacity for quality of life. They may say they only need to know how you feel about resuscitation, but you are within your rights to insist you also want them to know about a power of attorney and plans for your children, as they may be the first to be in a position to respond and contact the right people. Note that if you also have a power of attorney for health and care decisions, the most recent of these will be the one that is legally binding. If you are making an advance directive, make sure you state clearly that you want your attorney to be consulted for all decisions.

The best resource for living wills and advance care planning is Compassion in Dying (4), who provide widely accepted templates and a telephone advice service.

## 11.6 Financial planning

Most of us will have grown up in the welfare state, knowing that there are resources to turn to when we need them – free state education, social housing, health care and benefits – the safety net, in other words. Since the nineteen eighties, there has been a steady change in the political climate, and as I write some resources are already no longer available, others are being withdrawn and more are under threat. I have recently discovered that neither chiropody nor physiotherapy are provided free in my area, unless you have a listed condition. These services are ones which we are more likely to need with age. We have not necessarily adjusted to the practical implication of this in a timely manner. The very rich have always been cushioned by capital and often used private services anyway, but most of us need to consider diverting significant sums to the savings, insurance and pension schemes we are going to need to replace the state provisions we grew up with. I must admit to being one of those people who did not take this on board, and the reality hit me hard when I lost my job at the age of 59 and had to claim jobseekers allowance for only the second time in my life. Having never earned a high salary, I felt totally ignorant of the ways in which I might have been better prepared, and had to seek advice from others.

The main message is to save as much as you can afford. Work out a sum, and then work out your priorities – health, pension, education, replacing the boiler, or just a lump sum for eventualities. If this all seems overwhelming and alien, you can ask an Independent Financial Adviser (IFA) to help. This might be available through your trade union, if you are a member.

If you are concerned by the politics of financial investments, you can insist on ethical options and providers. An IFA can charge you directly for their service or claim a commission from the products you choose, so you do not need to have the cash up front. If you need help to navigate this alone, there is plenty of help online and in print. I recommend the Martin Lewis Money Saving Expert, Money Advice Service, and Which? resources, as well as Gingerbread, although the quality of resources can change over time.

How much can you afford? If you have always saved, this is easy. All you need to do is consider if you could be diverting your savings into better resources for your future needs, and if you can save enough to diversify. If you have never been in the habit of saving and never have much left over when payday comes, now is the time to make changes. First, consider small ways you can spend less – how often do you buy a takeaway coffee or magazine, or the best brand ice cream or cosmetics? Would the reassurance of future security be worth the sacrifice? The price of two coffees and a glossy magazine a week could be a meaningful sum to put away; diverting small sums is the best start. There are many budgeting apps and online services to help if you need guidance, just make sure you are using one that has no commercial interest in your money! Have a look at Money Advice or MoneySavingExpert for advice on how to track your spending. If you are more aware of where your money is going, you will have greater choice (and motivation) to change it.

**What are your priorities?**

- An emergency fund – for the replacement of essentials such as the car, the boiler or washing machine
- Health and disability / critical Illness cover – look for a product that will cover the cost of childcare if you were hospitalised or incapacitated. Some employers subsidise such schemes for their staff, on the basis that it might shorten absences. If there are no other provisions, care home fees will ultimately be re-couped from your estate when you die, which usually means selling your home.
- Life insurance – this will pay out a lump sum on your death, which could help your guardian support your child, or pay for their higher education
- Pension / additional contributions – so you can retire without worrying about income, or not fear becoming dependent on your child
- Education – higher education costs more than the fees that are covered by grants and loans, even if your child gets the maximum entitlement
- Housing – to pay off your mortgage or move to have more space
- A nest egg for your child – for a first car or deposit for a home.

Many large employers and public services offer free or cut-price private insurance and / or health cover. Even if you are against this in principle and unwilling to use the private health care itself, it often includes the cost of childcare and help with basic housework that you would need if you are in hospital or convalescing.

It is critical to recognise our children's need to develop their own financial knowhow, including an understanding of the social pressures they will be subject to, the power of advertising and the media, and simple financial management and decision making. It is no longer necessary to pretend that money is a dirty topic, we can involve our children in the day-to-day decisions we have to make, as well as giving them space to learn how to make their own choices. Martin Lewis' Money Saving Expert and the Money Advice Service (5, 6, 7, 8) have resources online, but there may be local organisations that provide active support. Your nearest Citizens Advice or public library should have the details.

This chapter may strike you as bleak or negative, but these are vital things to consider. You may be lucky and have never experienced setbacks or hardships prior to becoming a mum. It takes considerable energy to suppress any thought of possible problems, and if you take some steps to address the potential difficulties, you may be surprised at the relief it brings.

## References


1. Children and Family Court Advisory and Support Service (Cafcass): www.cafcass.gov.uk
2. Office of the Public Guardian: www.gov.uk/government/organisations/office-of the-public-guardian
3. Power of Attorney forms: www.gov.uk/power-of-attorney (beware of similar sounding websites that charge to complete the forms for you)
4. For living wills and advance care planning: mydecisions.org.uk/
5. www.moneysavingexpert.com/family/
6. www.moneyadviceservice.org.uk/en
7. https://www.fincap.org.uk/
8. https://medium.com/s/story/7-strategies-for-raising-kids-to-be-good-at-money-3c1f9f9455b5

# Appendix 1: Who are the Solo Mums?

## Solo Mum Survey

Having decided to go ahead and create a family on my own in 1991, I found a group of others who had made the same decision. This became the DIY group, a support network that led to my interest in the diversity among this like-minded band of women. Our numbers have grown steadily, but the research lags behind.

On the medical side, the right questions have not been asked consistently. Some years the HFEA offer a 'no partner' option as cause of infertility, but others might list themselves under other headings if they also had a medical reason. A large number is also included as 'patient unexplained', some of whom may be single women who fear their status might prejudice their access to help, or clinics concerned about the risk of publicity.

On the part of academic research, samples have been too small to sustain rigorous study, as many single women wish to avoid publicity to protect their privacy, and their children's. Once a single woman has a child, she is also likely to have more demands on her time than a woman with a partner, and less time to contribute to research. Finally, I was also told (informally) that because most of the studies have shown little of note, it has become more difficult to obtain research funding.

## Survey Methods

In my role coordinating the DCN's service to single women, I had access to the 650+ women members, so from December 2015 to February 2016, I carried out a survey to investigate some of the stereotypes popular in the media and to establish some insight into who we are. Two hundred and twenty five women completed the survey. I designed it without any specialist advice, but the responses are interesting and useful, if not strictly conclusive.

Another factor for which I must apologise is failing to include any question about ethnic origins. My impression is that this group of women is predominantly white, though a significant number have origins abroad. The white European, American and Australasian women have often come to live in Britain as adults, while the Asian, African and African Caribbean women are more often from settled second or further generation families. There will be differences in the degree of community and family support, and in the individual personality traits associated with making such a decision, which are an important area for further study. It would be useful to know about the specific support needs of women from minority or marginalised communities.

**Summary of Findings**

The survey was completed by 225 respondents. The results show wide diversity: the stereotypes are not always true and there are always contrasting exceptions. It is these exceptions that are often more interesting – it is hard to generalise. The important fact of the impact on our children is omitted in this survey.

There was a great deal of satisfaction with the treatment the women who responded had received, although there were also reports of difficulties and complaints. We are generally well educated and trained and earning average or higher incomes, but many of us also reduce our work commitments once our children arrive, and our earnings reflect this. We mostly have stable housing, though many of us need to move in order to provide a more suitable home for a child. The stereotype of the 'must have it all' 'high-flying professional' does not apply to most of us, though some of us may have lived this life before we made the decision to have a family. Decisiveness and resilience might be common features that help us to make the choice and survive the challenges of achieving success.

Three in ten of us report having deliberated for over two years before making the decision, and five in ten spent more than a year considering it. This suggests that it is a well-considered choice for which we evaluate and plan carefully. In other words, we mostly recognise it is an onerous long-term commitment that will change our lives.

The common suggestion that it is a selfish choice is inconsistent with the fact that most of us are giving up valued resources such as time, income and freedom by taking this step. I am not sure I understand which reasons for having a baby might be more virtuous or altruistic anyway. Certainly, most of us will agree that having a baby to cement a relationship, or to please our elders, or to meet traditional expectations, or to escape from the world of paid employment, are not great reasons to bring a child into the world. Having a baby to nurture and love and to raise to become a happy person, should be a universal reason, whatever our status.

Thoughtful deliberation, decisiveness and resilience might be common features, allowing us to make the choice and achieve our goals despite all the pressures and conventions we face.

I will look at the outcomes of the survey next. Then I will identify where further research might be useful, to fill the gaps and answer questions, as well as to track changes in the rapidly changing world both of assisted conception and of social support structure and culture.

## Survey Results

1. Fertility Treatment

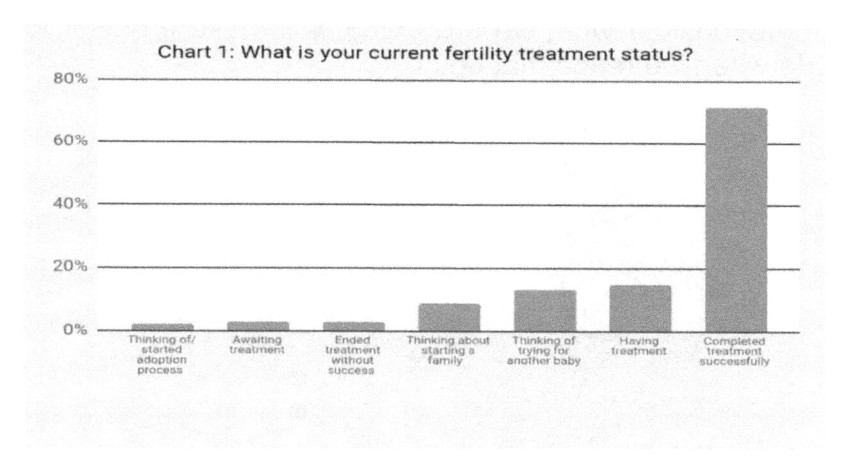


Of the 162 women who answered this question, 72% were pregnant or had successfully completed treatment and given birth, with 13% considering having a second baby. 25% of those who answered were still considering or trying to start a family, and 3% had given up the idea.

Several women mentioned having frozen embryos standing by in case they decide to have a second child, but there were no questions addressing this option directly.

One area that is poorly researched is the group of women who give up. It would be helpful to know what led to this decision, but obviously, most of them are reluctant to discuss, they want to move on. For those of us at the start of this process, it's valuable to be warned that it can be arduous and there are no guarantees, although few will be able to set themselves clear limits until they have experienced the process. Being aware that we may change plans, what our limits are: how much time or money, or how many times we are willing to reconsider what we are doing, will make it easier to do when we reach that point.

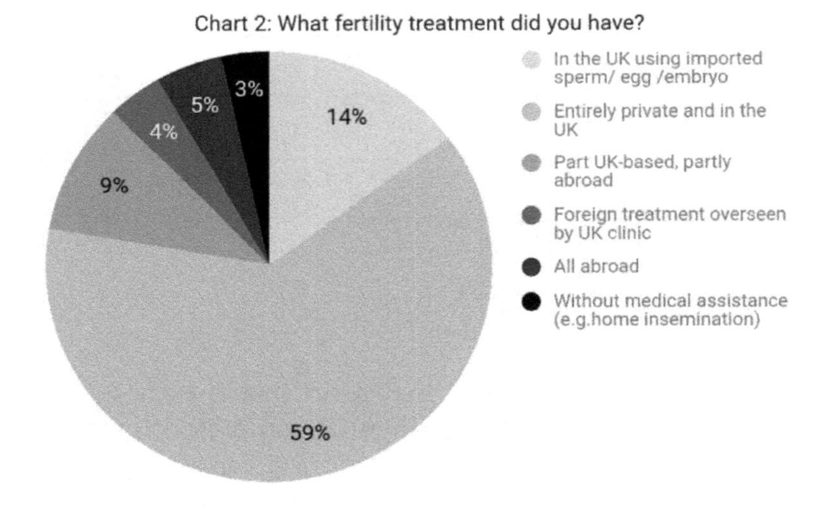


In most areas, the age restrictions to NHS treatment effectively bar most single women, and many women are unaware that there is any chance of treatment on the NHS at all. There was no question about using NHS facilities as a private patient, which some women reported in the 'comments' box: this could do with further research, as it may be a preferred option if more women know about it.

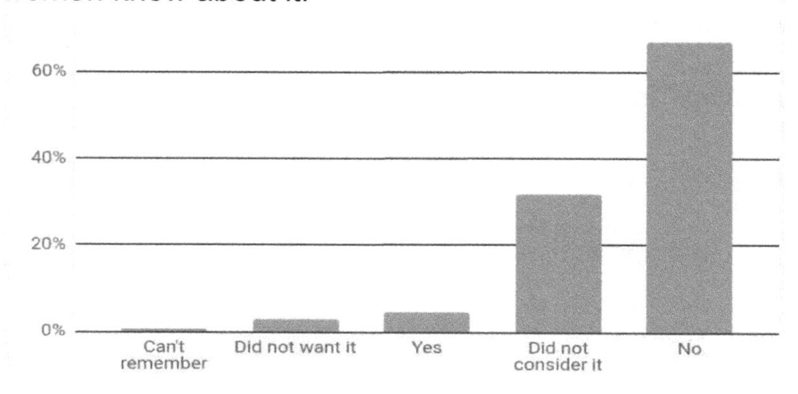


Of the 212 women who answered this question, 67% report never having been offered NHS treatment. 4.5% were offered it, of whom 2.8% did not want it.

Date of treatment:

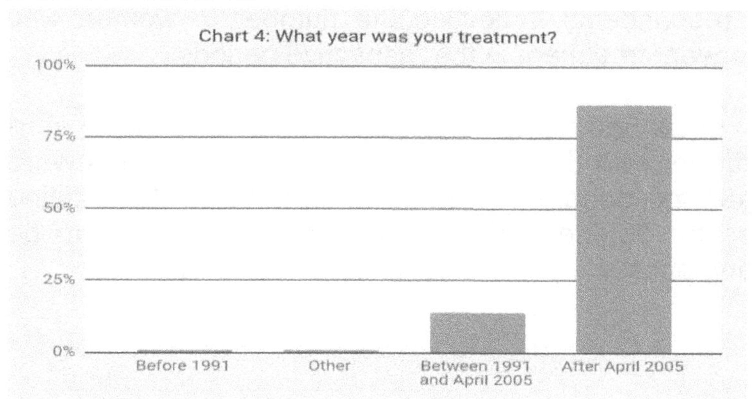

The vast majority of the women who answered the survey had their treatment after anonymity for donors was withdrawn in 2005

Waiting Times

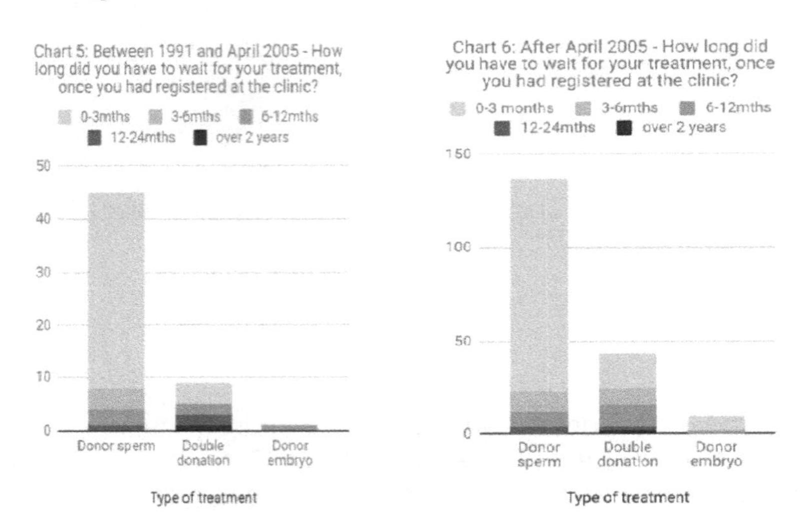


Chart 5 was answered by 55 respondents, and chart 6 by 187 respondents, reflecting the number of women who underwent treatment in the respective periods.

Few of us had to wait more than three months to start treatment with donor sperm, though waiting times were longer for double, or embryo, donation. The waiting times for double and embryo donation appears to be getting shorter.

## 2. Fertility Counselling

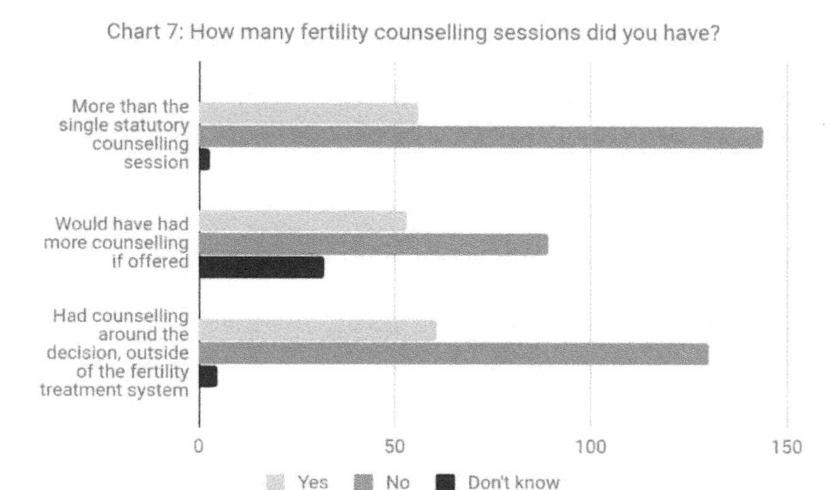


Half of the 201 women who answered this question did not want any more counselling than was offered, but a third also had private counselling or therapy relating to this decision. Three women do not remember ever being offered any counselling. Several women reported their appreciation for the support they were given, clinic based and outside the clinical setting.

Some women were dissatisfied with the clinic counselling. For instance:

- One disastrous session recently on 'end of the road' vs. one more go…
- I was unhappy with the obligatory session – unprofessional, lack of confidentiality, style…

- It didn't feel like counselling at all, more like being told about obligations and research and what's best for the child. I got much better support from the counsellor at my local hospital.
- I found the counsellor very unhelpful and made a formal complaint.

However, others report having had excellent support from their clinic counsellor, so it does seem to depend both on the individual's needs and the particular counsellor.

## 3. Discrimination

Chart 8: Did being single affect the service you were offered?

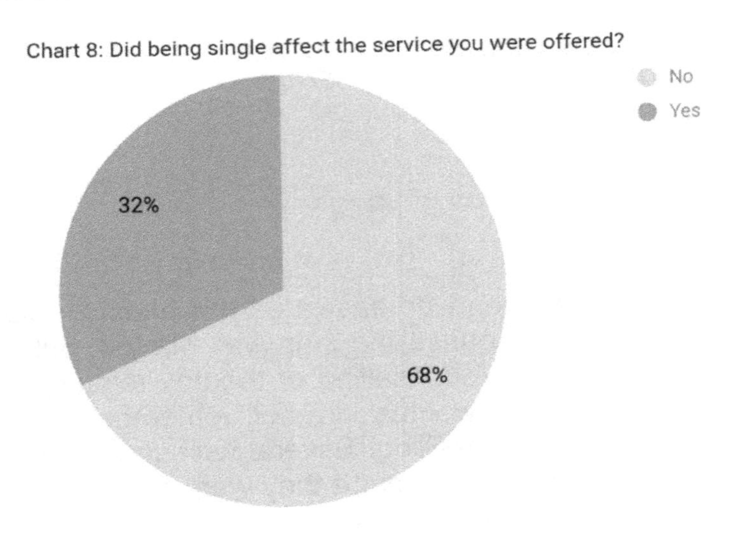


Of the 204 women who answered this question, 32% felt that being single had affected their treatment, 68% felt that it had not. However, some of the incidents reported by those who had felt discrimination sound serious. Many of these women will be reluctant to jeopardise their treatment by making a complaint, and/or will be in a location where there is no alternative to the clinic they are using. Note that these incidents may become rarer as the centres get used to more single women seeking treatment.

Some examples are:

- being told that she would have a longer wait than most because some of the consultants would not deal with her on ethical grounds
- being point blank refused treatment (in an NHS hospital) even though she had frozen eggs stored in their clinic
- being lectured on the 'immorality' of her decision
- GPs refusing to do any of the tests as she did not technically have a medical problem
- Having her choice of donor rejected as he had specifically stated he did not consent to it being used by a single woman, and they had not checked before offering it to her.

## 4. Treatment outside the UK

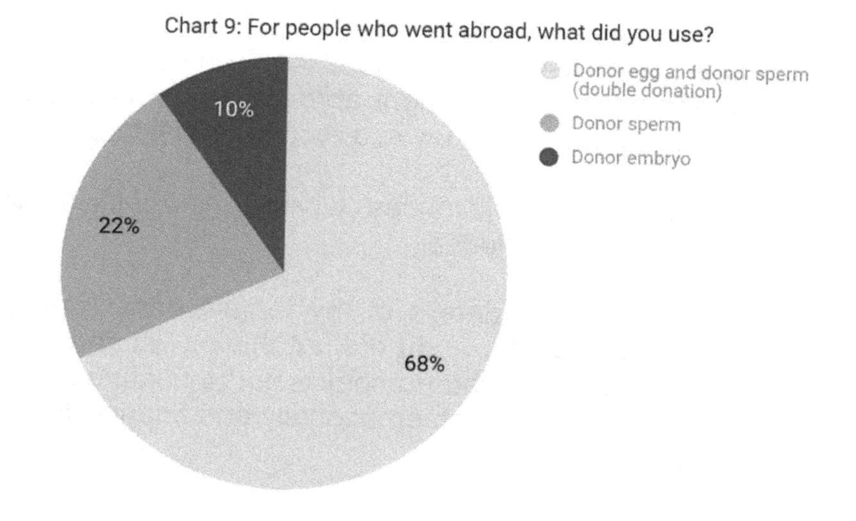

Thirty one women answered this question. The evidence shows that most women go abroad because of the shortage of double or embryo donation in the UK.

Two of the women volunteered the information that they were living abroad at the time and were treated locally.

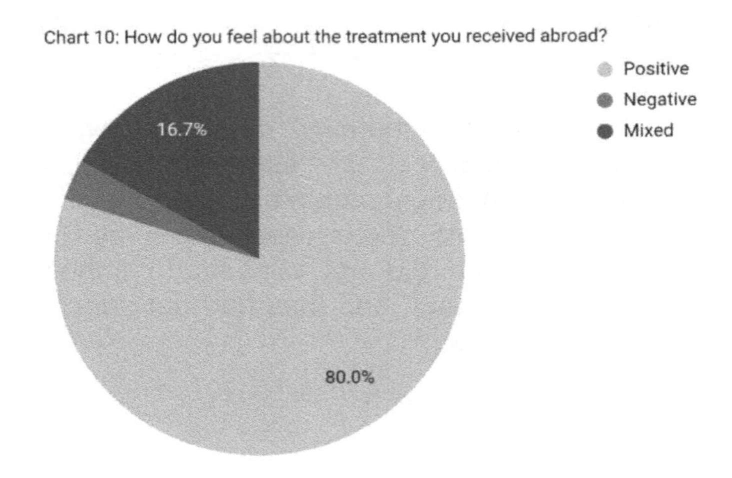


Thirty women answered this question. The vast majority of women who had treatment abroad were very happy with their experience and would recommend it to others.

Examples of the grievances women had with their treatment abroad included:

- I was not given details of my female donor until I arrived for transfer and I did not think it was a good match but I felt I had no choice but to continue as I had invested so much emotionally and financially on the cycle.

- Horrified: Clinic abroad stole around US$5K (they said they hadn't received a wire transfer, I paid again by card, they admitted that they'd received both, and I had to get a lawyer to have the US$5K overpayment returned).

Thirty women answered this question.

Chart 12: Did you, or would you, have used identity release gametes if available?

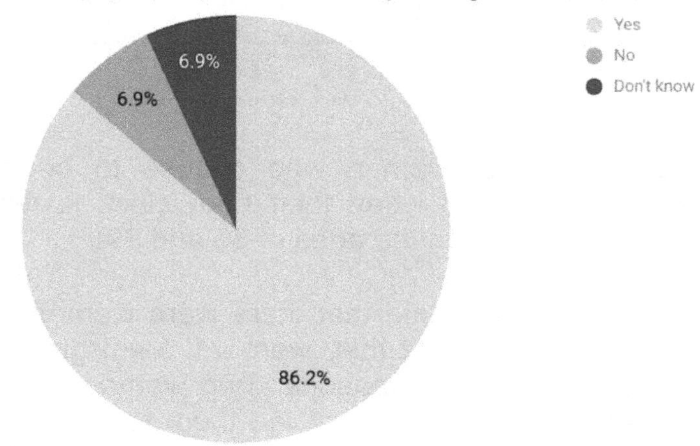

Twenty-nine women answered this question. Until 2005, UK sperm was anonymous, so some women chose to import or travel for ID release sperm, or simply to have greater choice. Nowadays, the situation is reversed as women usually travel because of the shorter waiting times and lower cost. Often the countries used have less donor choice and no ID release option, but cutting waiting times feels imperative as these women are on average older than those with partners.

5. Becoming a Solo Mum

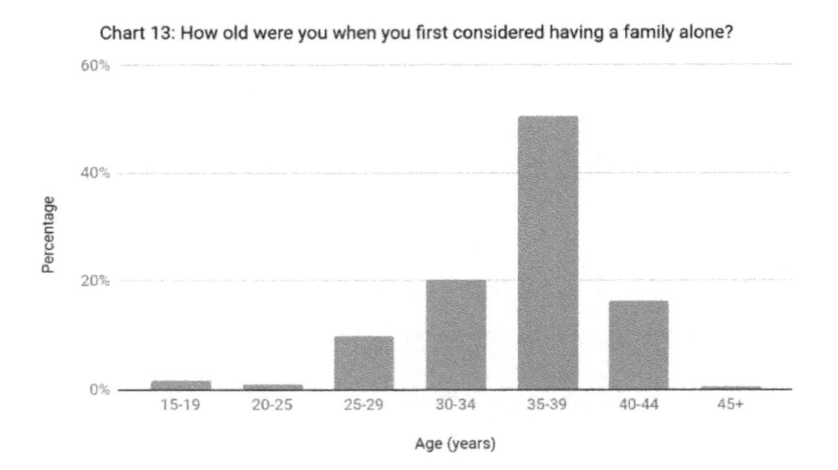


As expected, most women who choose to become single mothers do so when their body-clock is telling them it's time (between the ages of 35 and 39).

However, I was surprised that there were women who first considered it before they were 21. I am guessing that there were specific reasons. Two women told me their experience of early abuse led them to this choice before they had considered any other option. I was equally surprised to find that fifteen women did not consider this option until they reached 40. This suggests a poor understanding of the decline of fertility, of which many women said they wish they had been better warned.

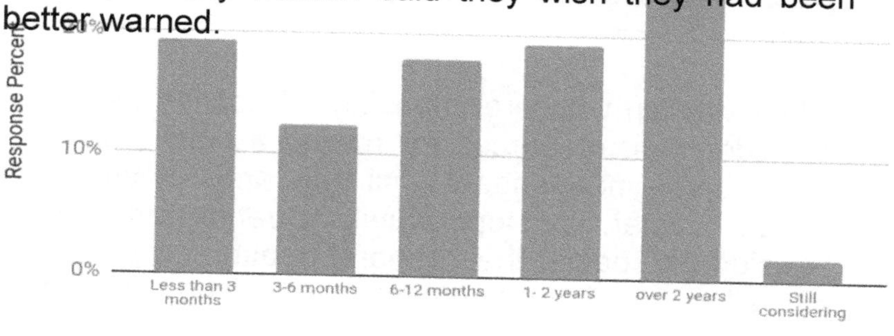


Nearly a third of the women surveyed took over two years to make the decision, but nearly a fifth took less than three months. This suggests that many women spend a long time considering this option before they go ahead. This could be due to reluctance to give up hope for the fairy tale family, as well as the time it takes to gather the information and think it through before reaching the conclusion.

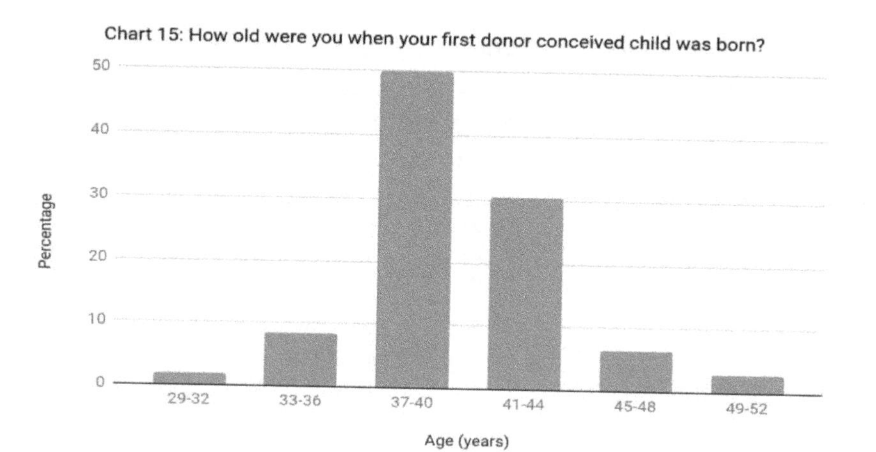


Chart 15: How old were you when your first donor conceived child was born?

The majority of single women were between 37 and 44 when they gave birth to their first donor conceived child. Only 7% were over 46, of whom three were 50 plus. Thus, we are relatively mature - no surprises there.

Older women who are choosing this option need to consider their resources for raising a child who will not become independent until they are in their mid-sixties or later: their opportunity to retire early, their pension prospects, their general health and stamina as well as the support network they can turn to if they should need help. Every mother I have ever spoken to expresses the fact that raising a child was more demanding and tiring than she had expected. Tiredness is simply a guaranteed fact of life for parents. I doubt that stating this here will change anybody's mind, but it might help bear the reality and not feel to blame or at fault for the inevitable. Many young mothers in their 20s certainly complain of exhaustion too, it's not all due to age, though ill-health won't help.

Twenty-nine women had more than one child, including four mothers with twins. Eleven of them had a first child from a previous relationship, and eighteen had a second donor conceived child. Outside the group who took part in the survey, I also know women who adopted a second child and who had a child in a relationship that started after their donor conceived child was born, so all variants are possible, having one donor conceived child leaves every other option still open, apart from getting younger!

## 6. Profile of the Solo Mums

### Income:

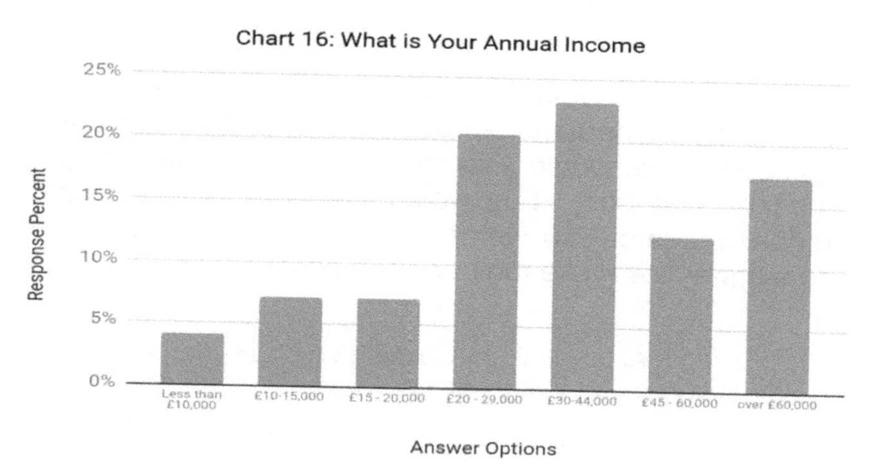


177 women answered this question. The average full-time salary in 2015 was £27,600. This survey was taken in December 2015 to February 2016, so the average may have risen slightly, but it looks like over 50% of respondents were earning above the average, so a comfortable, rather than wealthy group. Eighteen of the respondents were on reduced income due to maternity leave.

The distribution of income seems more even than in the general population. More than half the respondents earned well over the average income (17% earning more than twice the average), but over a quarter earned less than two-thirds of the average.

The explanation may lie in the fact that many of us have achieved a good standard of living by the time we start our families, and maintaining it can be achieved on a relatively low income, for instance if the mortgage is paid off. Evidently, while some choose to scale down, others can sustain a healthy income that covers the childcare costs to allowing them to continue their work.

Several women volunteered the information that they had given up demanding careers and re-trained to do something that would give them more time and energy for their child(ren). This would warrant clarification in further research, so women can see the longer term consequences make their choices accordingly.

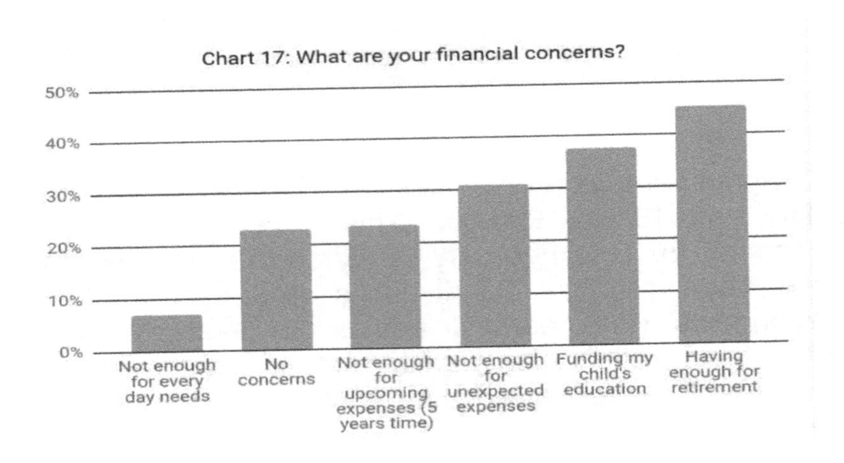


Financial concerns:
Most of us had some level of financial concerns, but 23% had none. Many had more than one area of concern, the biggest being retirement. It is significant that in the lifetime of this group, mostly born after 1975, many public services have been cut back or withdrawn. We grew up believing that we would have reasonable pensions and that our children would benefit from free education and health provisions. This is no longer guaranteed, but many of us have not adapted in time to ensure good private provisions. We need to inform

those who follow to start making the required savings early enough.

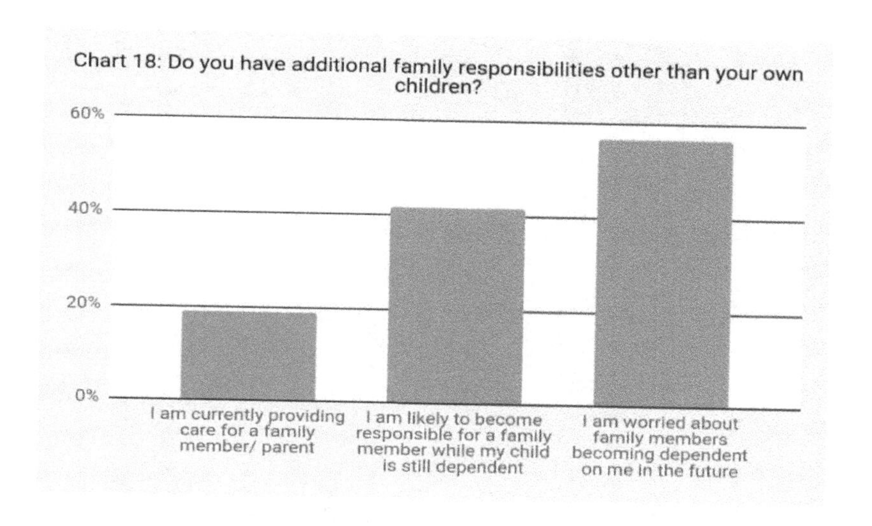


Family responsibilities:

Many women expected to become responsible for ageing parents before their children were grown up, with 20% already providing some care. We are particularly prone to finding ourselves in the 'sandwich generation', where there is an overlap between raising our children and caring for our elderly parents, when we are already at the age most would be retiring from work. In many cases, being the childless daughter meant we took this role on before we had children, so our siblings may feel they do not have an equal responsibility. This may be a subject worth exploring with them before it becomes too late to reverse.

Housing:

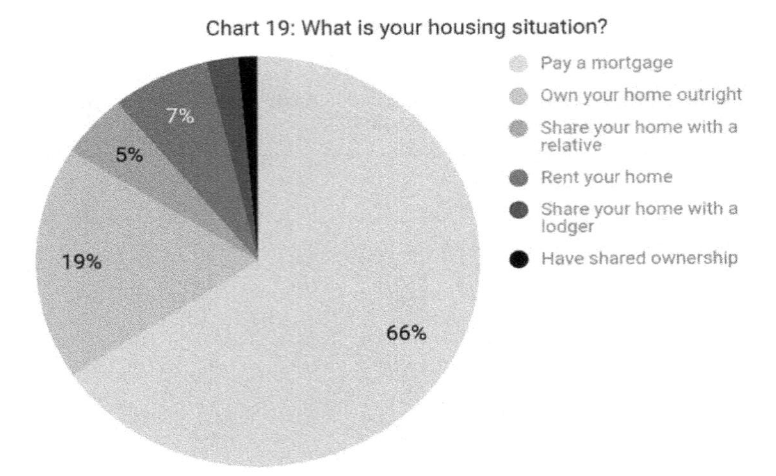


177 women answered this question. Several women reported that housing was an important issue to resolve before they started trying to get pregnant.

Education

Chart 20: What is your highest academic qualification?

4%
7%
10%
34%
46%

Doctorate
Masters Degree
Higher education - Bachelors degree
Further Education Diploma/ Certificate
Secondary education

In this respect, we seem to be a well-educated group. It is not easy to find data on qualification levels for the general population in the UK, but figures from Higher Education Student Data (www.hesa.ac.uk/news/11-01-2018/sfr247-higher-education-studentstatistics/quailfications) for Sept. 2017, show that 42% of the UK population aged 21 to 64 had achieved higher education qualifications, compared to 89% in this group.

## Conclusions:

- The conclusions I can draw from this is that we are after all a diverse group of women with a few things in common.
- We are on average older and better educated than the typical first time mother, though not always well-off. This may because we have already achieved our professional ambitions and are willing to compromise on material things, in other words a lifestyle choice.
- General knowledge about age and fertility needs to be better disseminated, to reduce the incidence of women not considering their options until they are running out.
- Housing and the care of ageing parents are often a worry.
- Counselling needs to be more consistently encouraged, and greater choice offered so that women can find someone who 'fits' and avoid negative experiences.
- Nearly all the women who had treatment abroad believed that identity release donors were preferable, although this might reflect the fact they were all DCN members. The DCN strongly advocates for openness about donors and

against anonymity, so those who do not feel comfortable with either of these may not join, or leave when they feel they don't fit in.

- The inequity of NHS provisions needs to be addressed. It affects all those who need fertility treatment, but single women are especially disadvantaged as CCG's have the discretion to set upper age limits and other barriers which exclude single women disproportionately.

## Further Research:

- Women from BAME communities – how do their experiences differ? Do they receive support from their family / communities (interesting to look at cultures where there is a strong matrilineal support system).
- How many women change career as part of the process of becoming mothers? What is the long term impact of this?
- Are there personality traits (resilience, decisiveness?) common to women who make this choice?
- Treatment abroad: are UK clinics referring single women to sister-clinics abroad? Is that because it's simpler than recruiting donors locally? How does that affect the cost / fees?
- Women who give up: understandably, women who give up trying to have a family are not keen on participating in any research. The loss of hope is deeply distressing, all the more so because the services tend to be so positive and encouraging and many women never consider the possibility of failure until they have experienced it repeatedly. It would be useful to know how long / how many options they tried and how often it's because of:

- Finances running out
- Giving up hope of success
- Age
- Doubts about whether it's the right thing for them
- It would be interesting to repeat this research every few years to track how the situation changes, as treatment options and the social context we live in are changing all the time.

## Appendix 2: What if your child is disabled?

Jane Sharp

I'm less than two years from my child turning 18 years old when she'll be able to ask for full details of her "willing to be known" US donor. While I was pregnant it was all I could think about: whose baby was I carrying? Whose genetics had I mixed with mine?

When my daughter was born that all went out the window. She was MY baby – every bit mine as if I had conceived her with a man I could see and touch. I loved her unconditionally and frankly didn't care less about her genetic father I was so overwhelmed with love for my baby. I never gave him another thought.

But now, my daughter's nearly 18 and she's mentally incapable of understanding her situation as she has complex disabilities and requires lifetime care. And here I am, suddenly increasingly wondering again where it all began, how and why, but I have no rights to make any enquiry. So what about my life? My mental health? I've been through so much and face so much with my daughter's future to secure after I'm gone, and yet I must live with never knowing whose genes I mixed mine with, who's baby I carried, and all because she's so damaged.

I feel like I'm being doubly punished for her condition. I deliberately chose a "willing to be known" donor not just for my daughter's sake but for mine too. But I'll never know. My daughter won't even be able to easily trace her siblings like others could. We're both being punished. Don't think I want to know my daughter's donor so I can lay blame for her condition at his door. I willingly and happily signed all the documents to ensure the donor needn't worry about me chasing him for money or parental rights or a medical lawsuit. Why then should I be denied the name and a photo of the donor I used? His healthy children will be allowed to know, and through them supposedly the mothers, but my daughter can't know, not even for her medical records, and neither can I. It feels like an added injustice and I feel so sad for my baby. Have private genetic counselling before going ahead with the treatment.

I now know the gene pool I created for my child was far more likely than others to create the lifetime complex special needs she has today. Always choose a donor with many healthy offspring. Not only have the donor's genes been "tested" successfully with many different gene pool combinations, but it also means more half siblings may be traceable in the future. When I was choosing my donor the only advice I was given was not to choose a CMV positive donor as I have never been exposed to the virus. That severely limited the number of donors I could choose from as it seems most people have come across this flu-like virus at some point in their lives.

I took the advice to heart and never questioned it, but I now know the chance of my catching CMV while pregnant (which could cause damage to my baby) was miniscule since I'd avoided it for 41 years despite working in major cities and doing extensive globe-trotting. Women who conceive with their partners don't check for this virus so why was I so hung up about it? I don't think I would have chosen my donor had I had more choice. Would my daughter still have been born with complex special needs? I'll never know for sure, but certainly my chosen donor's medical profile wasn't the best I could have picked.

My experience of sibling tracing using official channels has been mixed. Two families responded but it is hard to get them to keep in touch. Though their children share some of my daughter's complex special needs the families don't share my desire to swap information to help support our children better. The mothers are in relationships and have other children, and they live abroad, whereas I'm a single parent and older too so we don't have much in common at all. Don't assume all sibling families are happy to share more than just a name even if they go to the trouble of tracing you.

I would never advise a woman not to have a child alone or by sperm donor because it may create a child requiring lifetime care as with my daughter, but I would strongly advise being counselled about it beforehand. It happens, and it happens to people of all ages and classes and however super fit you are. Take off the rose tinted spectacles and consider how you'd cope if it happened to you.

What arrangements could you put in place? What support do you have, what money, what future? Yes I considered what I'd do if my baby was disabled, but only to the extent of having tests when she was inside me. When they were all clear, I sailed ahead. But my daughter was born requiring lifetime care. That could happen to you. How would you cope?

## Appendix 3: Grateful to receive, glad to give - Emma's egg-sharing story

*This story was written by Emma in 2018 and first published in the DCNetwork journal.*

The constant in my life has been wanting to be a parent. Being gay, I've always known my family would be unconventional. I had hoped to create a family with a partner, but at the age of 33 I decided I didn't want to spend any more of my life without my child. It was my best decision. I am a solo mum to a daughter conceived with sperm donation. I am also an egg donor via egg sharing. I hadn't heard about egg donation before going for my own treatment, but it made perfect sense to share what I was lucky enough to have; especially as I was relying on someone else's kind donation.

Egg-sharing is sometimes positioned as the opposite of 'altruistic donation', as if it is motivated by self-interest or financial desperation. Yet during treatment, I felt invested for my recipient perhaps more than for myself. I feel the weight of the lifelong commitment I made with my donation: a commitment to be available should she need information, or more eggs, or want to make contact. Receiving donor sperm was for me an act of trust: that the clinic has done its research and used its judgement well; and that the donor has made a considered choice and will honour his commitments. Donating eggs was a similar act of trust: that the recipient(s) - about whom I know nothing at all - will be good parent(s); that they will tell their child that they are donor conceived;

that they will support their child in whatever they choose to do.

My child and I sit on both sides of the donor conception experience, and it's an interesting journey. As a donor conceived child, my daughter has the right to information, and to choose to make contact. As the child of a donor, she does not have these rights. I struggle with this sometimes: the consequence for her of my decision to donate. She's only young, and I do not yet know how she will feel. I worry about the complexity of her potential network, while feeling that we need to jump feet first into this complexity... with nine potential other UK families via her sperm donor, and an unlimited number of families overseas, we have space to welcome one family via egg donation into her story. And then there is my embryo on ice. I have everything I wished for in my daughter. But can I donate this embryo, her full genetic sibling? I'm not yet sure.

There is complexity, certainly. But there is also connection. Through donor conception, and DC Network, we have met dear friends and key supporters. We have received donated breast milk when my daughter was a day-old infant. We have met the childminder to whom I entrust my daughter's care. Through shared solo-motherhood, we know the people who are at our door when I am sick or need help.

And we are connected, too, to these people we have never met, in a circle of life. On the night my daughter was born, my heart was full. Full of love for my perfect baby. Full of gratitude for her donor, who gave life to my child. And full of good wishes for my recipient, who I hoped was experiencing her own moment like this, wherever she is. My daughter is the joy of my life. I hope hers is too.

## Appendix 4: Lottie's Story: How she came to have a known donor and a voluntary dad

Lottie, my daughter now age 12, was born in 2003: I was then 50. She was conceived through IVF with a known donor sperm and an egg-share donor egg·

**Going to a clinic for treatment**
As a single woman with a history of depression, I was not accepted by the first clinic I applied to. However, with the help of a fertility consultant in the north of England, I found my way to an open-minded London clinic who accepted me with my doctor's written declaration that I was 'stable'.

The first IVF attempt was with my own egg and an unknown donor I chose from my clinic's brief descriptions of the men in their sperm bank. This attempt was not thought likely to succeed because of my age (mid-forties) and it did not.

However I did realise then how much I minded having an anonymous donor when there were some nice men in my acquaintance, current and past, that I would have been happy to have as genetic father for my child.

**Finding a known donor**
Having a known donor seemed particularly important for my next step, which was to go on the egg donor waiting list at my clinic – having an egg donor also would give me a greatly improved chance of success but would mean no knowledge of genetic history and

family on the female side as well as the male side. (I wanted to avoid this if I could.)

For a while I considered who I might ask from the men I knew, whether they might donate for me. During this time I met again someone I had been briefly involved with in the past, (who was now in a stable relationship but had never had a child) - he surprised me by showing interest in being a donor for the child I was trying for. However for my clinic it was a condition of using any known donor with a partner that their partner agree, and he was totally unwilling to ask her.

Then Billy, a friend I met through motorbiking, said he would help me in this – he himself did not want children however he was willing to be a donor for me. He did not see himself as having much contact in the future with any child born from his sperm.

Billy was a likeable person with qualities to value and some talent in art and music as well as ability in building bikes, also somewhat younger than me, which seemed a good idea. He was in his late thirties. He smoked but did not drink much alcohol, only loads of coffee - which it seems is good for sperm as it makes them 'much more active' according to what Lottie has been taught recently at school.

I thought it important that Billy should be willing to tell his family if his donation of sperm led to a child being born, and, as he agreed to this, I arranged for him to visit my London clinic to be interviewed and his sperm tested. This went through okay and he visited the clinic two or three times more, as far as I recall, to donate sperm, which was then frozen and stored for when it might be needed.

**Waiting for donor eggs**

From this time, it was several more years before the next step could be taken. The egg donor waiting list hardly moved for at least 3 years, then suddenly my clinic introduced an egg sharing scheme whereby the would-be recipient of eggs paid for the treatment of a younger woman wanting IVF herself but with good eggs. I signed up for this at once and accepted several egg donors in turn before one worked out, what with cycles and harvest of eggs etc.

**An embryo embedding**

In September 2002 Billy's sperm was put with the 3 eggs I received from my egg-share donor, and 2 embryos were created. These were implanted and I awaited the outcome, but I knew this would be my last attempt and I tried to help the process along by going to a Reiki healer to help the embryos embed. At the time the healer felt her treatment was successful - she said she felt a connection and I also had an elated and excited feeling. Fantastically (to me) one embryo embedded in my womb and was born June 2003 as my dear baby 'Lottie'.

Finding a male influence for Lottie's growing up

At the same time, my clinic had made it a condition that as a single mother I should seek to ensure a male influence in my child's life. Billy had made it clear he did not want this role and when by chance I met someone who did want to help bring up a child – we briefly tried a relationship but it did not quite work - I was glad that he should be a voluntary 'dad' for my daughter as he also had qualities I valued, though he was very different from me. His name here is 'Guy'.

Billy was happy that Guy should be the 'dad', albeit a very part-time dad with limited access and responsibilities, those being mostly to make my daughter feel loved and cared for by a man as well as a woman. (This Guy has done very well and also taught her many useful things and helped her grow up as well as she has. He has particularly given her a foothold in various sports she has found she enjoys and is good at, as I am not.)

Guy's involvement with my daughter has not always been easy for either Guy or me. Communication between us is sometimes a problem, but I have valued his being there for my daughter on the end of a phone particularly when I have had difficulties resolving situations with her or for her, or for visits in school holidays. I am glad of a break and it is good for her to be somewhere different with someone else who loves her.

**Contact with the male donor and his mum**

I stayed friends with Billy, who at that time lived not far away, and he saw Lottie now and then but did not get involved, it was more social. However when Billy's mum learnt of Lottie's birth, she said to me 'Lottie has a second grandmother' and sent Lottie a shawl she had crocheted for her herself. After that there were always birthday cards which we were glad of and I sent yearly photos.

Later Billy moved hundreds of miles away, to live with and look after his now increasingly disabled mother. We did not see him for some years, but lately I have become friends with his mum, (largely through talking on the phone as they live so far away) and we have been to see them twice. Lottie has been very happy with this development and particularly has a good rapport with Billy's mum, her genetic grandmother.

Billy has not been quite sure how he has come out of this but he is proud of Lottie's achievements – that she should have the chance to develop her potential was his main concern when he became a donor for her birth - and on our visits he has several times taken her out on the bike. He and Guy are both skilled workers and Lottie is practical, creative and academic by turn.

### Difficult years at school

Lottie did have some difficult years at her first primary school when she also had health problems. However I succeeded in changing her school to a more child-centred one, greatly helped by Lottie's clear wish to make the change once it became a possibility, and it worked out well, with a very supportive headmistress and a motivated and kindly team of staff. There were also other changes including in her health care and in time she got over her health problems. It was when she had largely got through these difficulties that we got better acquainted with Billy's mum also and first visited her and Lottie's genetic dad, Billy.

### Support network developing and overcoming of problems

My mum in Ireland has always been very supportive,

and now we have more of a relationship with Billy's mum also. She is a lovely person with a relaxed way about her despite her disabilities and with a good sense of humour.

Lottie and I share many interests and have many laughs. My depression has gradually got better over the years. We have both learnt through the overcoming of problems – we were helped in this by a couple of parenting courses I was lucky enough to find a place on.

Though the life of single parent and of a single parent's child can be problematic, especially in financial and organizational terms, many people have helped us including family, and particularly some of my long-term friends who have been helpful and supportive way beyond what could be expected.

**Catching up**

Also, we have met new friends and other people, including childminders, who have helped a lot, as did her final and exceptional childminder when she tutored Lottie in a catch-up student support programme that my mother shared the cost of. This allowed Lottie to make up for the years she was unhappy at her first school and not too receptive to their lessons.

**Being the sole legal parent**

I am thankful that our situation is simplified by my being the sole legal parent. Though this was not at all what I had wanted to happen in my ideal life plan, it was what I ended up with.

However it has advantages. As I was advised by a nurse when I went for treatment at my clinic, being the sole legal parent means that custody conflicts with an estranged partner will not happen, which is important to lessen insecurity.

**Lottie's life now**

Now in year two at her secondary school, Lottie finally likes school, has made friends there and is gaining in confidence. We are in touch with Billy's mum (and, through her, Billy) and we consider both them and Guy as part of our extended family. For Lottie, Guy is someone she particularly loves and calls 'Dad' - for me he is someone I have been able to count on to be there for Lottie as far as he could be, although he is some years older than me and now has a very serious health condition. Also in her life Lottie has a cat she loves dearly called 'Sock' and she says it is better without other siblings.

## Appendix 5: Notes from the empty nest...

Solo mothering was my primary identity for 18 years. It really began when I was 38 and made the decision to go ahead and have a baby on my own, since the usual avenues were not looking plausible any more. Three years of failed treatment cycles and two miscarriages later, he was finally born two weeks before my 42nd birthday.

None of the other elements of my life ended the day my son was born, but they all moved to the back seat, jostling each other (and me) from time to time. Basically he was the centre and the forefront, and everything else fit in around him.

I can't express adequately the wonder and joy of having him in my life. I feel privileged and lucky that I had the opportunity, that I had the child I did, and for every single aspect of it, even the tears and terrors.

Was it worth it? Every single second, including the three years on the treatment roller-coaster and all the dashed hopes and despair, the horrendous birth and months of zombiedom to recover, and the three years of broken nights that followed. The happiness he has brought into my life is immeasurable. Now that he's on his way to being his own person, the pride is overwhelming.

How does it compare to what I expected? I remember saying, to those who asked, that I had no idea what to expect except that my whole life would change forever. That has proven true.

**Things that never happened:**

- Nobody ever openly expressed their disapproval
- He never seriously grieved for a father, as far as I know. He did say it would be good to have one for various reasons (to play killing games with, or so I wouldn't have to go to work so much), which I could sympathise with, but he didn't blame me. I recognise that he might have just never wanted to upset me with these thoughts, but that suggests our relationship has been good enough for him not to need to blame or reject me.
- I never heard of him being teased about it either.
- He's never expressed much interest in the issue, even though he's seen me getting involved and heard about it plenty.

**Things I wasn't expecting:**

- How many people were impressed / delighted / positive and supportive about the choice I'd made.
- The many relationships I made in my neighbourhood with other new mums and the mutual support that we developed.
- That I could manage on much less money for the sake of having more time with my child. When I finally did go back to work, I went half-time, thinking I'd just do more hours when I needed the money. Eighteen years later, I was still only working 2/3 of a full week, and then I lost my job! Very happy to decide 'Never again!'

**The best and the worst?**

The best:

- The privilege of being part of his life from day one, watching him grow and learn and develop into a young man who is responsible, loveable, hardworking and enjoying his life.

- Being involved in his two year old passion for diggers, his teenage passion for mountains, and everything in between!
- Playing in the bath and reading bedtime stories.
- Taking him to football matches and all those things I'd never have done without him, and had such fun doing with him.

The worst:

- The unexpectedly hard decisions – choosing child care, nurseries and schools that nobody could help me with.
- Both of us being sick at the same time with a shared dose of Noro virus .
- His unhappiness with school for six months, and the subsequent blips of wondering / hoping we would get it right for him... All vindicated now that he's in his first job, with two degrees under his belt, on what promises to be a fulfilling career.

**What would I have done differently?**

- I'd have set up somewhere he could sit in the kitchen from day 1, so he could be more involved in what was going on there and we could eat together more often.
- I'd have involved him more in household chores, even after he stopped enjoying sweeping and hoovering – making sure he knew how to clean the toilet, iron a shirt and sew on a button before he went off to college.
- I'd have made sure he could cook more than one meal (and several fancy puddings) before he left home, and that he would boast about it too!
- I'd have made music a bigger part of our life,

**What have I learned?**

- I have learned with absolute certainty that children come into the world with their own agenda, so we may as well start from where they are rather than fight it. On the whole, they want to please, so that can be used to work out a solution to most things.

- I have learned to swallow my expectations and show my happiness and love of whoever my son becomes, as he changes and develops.
- I have learned not to get hurt by his adolescent need to distance himself from me, hoping he will find a comfortable distance eventually!
- I've learned that putting extra money into my pension was a great decision, allowing me to retire early and manage until I become entitled to my State Pension without too much pressure to take a paid job. Losing my job was shocking and demoralising, but it would have been much worse if there had been financial pressures.

**What next?**

- Now I am facing the rest of my life with him at best somewhere nearby, but no longer in the centre of my life and needing me there right behind him. The emotional burden is lifted as he develops his own relationships, so I am no longer his main source of love and support.
- I feel quite unprepared. I have a much smaller circle of friends than I used to have, and I need to do something about that.
- I no longer have a job to provide me with a separate identity, but I do have several projects, most of them solitary, so I need to do something about that.
- Having the house to myself has been great, and I've finally started catching up after 20 years of neglect, enjoying decorating and doing practical things.

It's happened much too quickly, but I'm finding that I do have the energy to work on the gaps that have appeared – this book for one thing, a new intimate relationship, free of the old baggage I used to impose on myself, and a more open view of how the last quarter of my life might roll out. The best bit, totally unexpected, is the fact that my family has now doubled not shrunk. I have Sunday dinners with four of us round the table, why did I never imagine that? Many of my friends are looking after grandchildren, which it's far too early for me to wish for, but having my family at my table fills me with pride and delight.

I wish the readers the best of luck, it's a tough road to choose but may it bring you great happiness as it has me.

Emily, March 2019

# Bibliography

## Books

Brockes, E.: An Excellent Choice, Panic and Joy on My Solo Path to Motherhood, Penguin Random House, 2018

Drexler, P.: Raising Boys without Men: How Maverick Moms Are Creating the Next Generation of Exceptional Men, Rodale Books, 2007

Eliot, L.: Pink Brain, Blue Brain: How Small Differences Grow into Troublesome Gaps — and What We Can Do About It, Houghton Mifflin, 2009

Faber, A. and Mazlich, E.: How to Talk So Kids Will Listen & Listen So Kids will Talk, Harper Collins, 2012

Fine, K. (ed.): Donor Conception for Life-Psychoanalytic Reflections on New Ways of Conceiving the Family, Karnac, 2015

Ford, M.: Navigating the Land of If: Understanding Infertility and Exploring Your Options, Seal Press, 2009

Golombok, S.: Parenting: what really counts? Routledge, 2000

Golombok, S.: Parents and Children in New Family Forms, Cambridge University Press, 2015

Hertz, R. and Nelson, M.: Random Families: Genetic Strangers, Sperm donor Siblings and the Creation of New Kin, Oxford UP, 2018

Kramer, W. and Cahn, N.: Finding our Families, Avery, 2013

Lamb, M.: Parenting and Child Development in 'Nontraditional' Families, Psychology Press, 1998

Lamb, M.: The Role of the Father in Child Development, Wiley, 2010

Leach, P.: The Essential First Year, DK, 2010

Mattes, J.: Single Mothers by Choice, Three Rivers Press, 1994

Morris, J. (ed): Alone Together- the Voices of single Mothers, Women's Press, 1992

Morrissette, M.: Choosing Single Motherhood: the Thinking Woman's Guide, Be-Mondo Publishing, 2005

Murray, J.: That's My Boy- a Modern Parent's Guide to Raising a Happy and Confident Son, Vermillion, 2003

Panettieri, G. and Hall, P.: The Single Mother's Guide to Raising Remarkable Boys, Adams Media, 2008

de Paolo, B.: Single Parents and their children: the good news no-one tells you, Create Space Publishing, 2015

Richards, M., Pennings, G. and Appleby, J. (eds): Reproductive Donation: Practice, Policy and Bio-Ethics, Cambridge University Press, 2012

Roberts, G.: Going Solo: My choice to become a single mother using a donor, Piatkus, due April 2019

Seligman, M.: The Optimistic child, Harper paperbacks, 1996

Sloan, L.: Knock Yourself Up: No Man? No Problem? Avery, 2007

Solomon, A.: Far from the Tree: Parents, Children and the Search for Identity, Scribner, 2012

Turner, S.: The Myths of Motherhood – how Culture Re-invents the Good Mother, Penguin, 1994

Weschler, T.: Taking Charge of Your Fertility, Vermillion, 2016

Wise, J.: Flying Solo: A single parent's adoption story, CoramBAAF, 2007

## Articles

Ashley, M.: Primary School Boys' Identity Formation and the Male Role Model: An exploration of sexual identity and gender identity in the UK through attachment theory, Sex Education: Sexuality, Society and Learning, Vol.3, Issue 3, 2003

Blyth, E. & Kramer,W.: My daddy's name is donor: read with caution BioNews July 9th 2010 https://www.bionews.org.uk/page_92455

Bravo Moreno, A. (PhD): Feminist & non-feminist single mothers by choice https://nsuworks.nova.edu/tqr/vol24/iss4/20/

Bravo Moreno, A.: Choice mums and children's education: Does feminism matter? A qualitative study, Qualitative Report 24 (4) 2019

Crawshaw, M., Daniels, K., Adams, D., Bourne, K., van Hoof, J., Kramer, W., Pasch, L. and Thorn, P.: Emerging models for facilitating contact between people genetically related through donor conception, Reproductive Bio-Medicine and Society, Nov, 2015

Feldman, R. et al: Parental Oxytocin and Early Caregiving, Neuropsychopharmacology, 38, 1154–1162, 2013

Feldman, R.: Fathers' Oxytocin Levels Develop Through Close Contact and Contribute to Bonding just as with Mothers, 2010, www.sciencedaily.com/releases/ 2010/08/ 100820101207.htm

Freeman, T., Appleby. J. and Jadva:, V.: Identifiable donors and siblings: implications for the future, Reproductive Donation, Practice Policy and Bio-Ethics, Richards, M., Pennings, G. and Appleby, J., Cambridge, 2012

Frith, L., Blyth, E., Crawshaw, M. and van den Akker, O.: Searching for 'relations' using a DNA linking register by adults conceived following sperm donation, BioSocieties, 13 (1), 2018

Geddes, L.:
https://mosaicscience.com/story/exploding-nuclear-family/ - an accessible review of the history of assisted reproduction and the implications, The Wellcome Trust, 2015

Golombok, S. and Badger, S.: Children Raised in Mother-Headed Families, 2010, Human Reproduction, 25, 150-157

Hilpern, K.: Donor Conception: I'd got to the bottom of the secret, The Guardian, Nov 5th, 2011:
www.theguardian.com/lifeandstyle/2011/nov/05/donor-conception-adult-secrets

Holmes, S.: Going Solo: Responding to press coverage about the 'elective single mum', Huffington Post, 21st September, 2015 and:
www.theguardian.com/commentisfree/2015/aug/18/anonymous-sperm-donation-is-flawed-just-ask-donor-conceived-children and:
http://www.huffingtonpost.co.uk/dr-su-holmes/elective-single-mum_b_8157908.html? 1442999653

Horler, L.: Sperm donors may want anonymity, but there are real kids out there, The Guardian, 17th August, 2005

Holmes, S.: The Solo Mum, Feminism and the Negotiation of 'Choice', Women's Studies International Forum, 69 (April 2018) 40 – 48

Int. Soc. on Genetic Genealogy articles on Wikipedia relating to donor conception:
https://isogg.org/wiki/DNA_testing_for_the_donor_

conceived and
https://isogg.org/wiki/Information_for_donor-conceived_people:_getting_ready_for_contact

Jadva et al: Mom by choice, single by life's circumstance, Findings from a large scale survey of the experiences of single mothers by choice, Hum Fertil (Camb), 2009 Dec, 12.4

Jadva, V., Freeman, T., Kramer, W. and Golombok, S.: Offspring's experiences of searching for and contacting their donor siblings and donor, Reproductive BioMedicine Online, 20, 2010: www.rbmojournal.com/article/S1472-6483(10)00002-7/pdf

Kramer, W.: A brief history of Donor Conception, Huffington Post, 5th October, 2016: www.huffingtonpost.com/wendy-kramer/a-brief-history-of-donor-conception_b_9814184. html?guccounter=1

Lamb, M.: Mothers, Fathers, Families and Circumstances: Factors Affecting Children's Adjustment, Applied Developmental Science, 2012, 16, 98-111

Rose, J., Cresswell, E. and Whipp, C. in www.mindingmatters.com/one-legacy-of-anonymous-sperm-donation/ - on the negative impact of discovering they were donor-conceived

Stevens, B.: Offspring (documentary), 1997, available on Vimeo: https://vimeo.com/128603400

Stevens, B.: Sperm Donation: Inside a Deeply Emotive World of Powerful Incentives, Polarised Views and

Heated Debate, The Independent, 13th September, 2015:

Stevens, B.: http://www.anonymousfathersday.com/2012/04/barry-stevens-biodad/

www.independent.co.uk/life-style/health-and-families/features/sperm-donation-inside-a-deeply-emotive-world-of-powerful-incentives-polarised-views-and-heated-10498925.html

www.whatisepigenetics.com/what-is-epigenetics/

## Websites and online resources

www.arc-uk.org Ante-natal Results and Choices: a National service with website and helpline to support you in decisions relating to antenatal testing.

www.bionews.org.uk online journal of the Progress Educational Trust (PET) providing news and comment on genetics, assisted conception and related areas.

Children's Adoption and Fostering Court Advisory Service: www.cafcass.gov.uk - independent body set up to defend the interests of children in Family Court proceedings.

https://corambaaf.org.uk/fostering-adoption the national agency overseeing adoption and fostering.

The Centre for Inter-Country Adoption (IAC)
www.icacentre.org.uk

Citizens Advice: www.citizensadvice.org.uk/benefits/benefits-introduction/what-benefits-can-i-get/

www.donorsiblingregistry.com US website, the biggest in the world, helping donors and offspring make connections.
The Facebook page for news and discussion is: www.facebook.com/pages/biz/non_profitDonor-Sibling-Registry-Connecting-Donor-Families-1460854104145782/

Donor Conceived Register (DCR): http://donorconceivedregister.org.uk/ Register for those born before the HFE Act 1991. In April 2018 the HFEA took over responsibility for running this register. The DCR service has been delivered by the NGDT (see below) but the contract ends on 31 March 2019: please check for current situation.

www.dcnetwork.org the website for the Donor Conception Network (DCN), a national charity in the UK for all families considering or created with donor conception. Includes a large number of single women (650+ in 2018).

Donor Sibling Link: www.hfea.gov.uk/donation/donor-conceived-people-and-their-parents/donor-sibling-link-dsl/ - The HFEA service for hose born since 1991 who want to trace other offspring from the same donor.

Fawcett Society: www.fawcettsociety.org.uk

www.fertilityfairness.co.uk campaigns against the 'post-code lottery' and for fair access for all to fertility treatment.

www.first4adoption.org.uk/being-an-adoptive-parent/how-do-i-decide/single-thinking-adoption/

www.gingerbread.org.uk the charity for single parent families - expert advice and practical support for single mums and dads in England and Wales.

www.hfea.gov.uk the Human Fertility and Embryology Authority website, with masses of impartial information including 'Choose a Fertility Clinic', information about treatment choices, information for donor offspring etc. Some meetings are open to the public- info on website.

International Society for Genetics in Genealogy have several articles relating to donor conception on their website: www.genealogywise.com/group/isogg

www.mind.org.uk/information-support/types-of-mental-health-problems/postnatal-depression.aspx#.Vk2TbHbhC00 Mind is the national organisation for mental health, with good local groups in most areas. The website has excellent information and advice on all aspects of mental health, including post-natal depression and child and adolescent mental health and support for carers.

www.moneyadviceservice.org.uk/en# good guide on debt and financial issues.

www.moneysavingexpert.com/family/ a wide ranging and up-to-date source of information on all things financial – consumer affairs, family finance.

www.moneysupermarket.com

www.nataliegambleassociates.co.uk/knowledge-centre- Law firm specialising in assisted conception and LGBT issues

www.nct.org.uk the National Childbirth Trust: a nationwide network of local groups providing ante-natal classes and support groups for new mums.

NGDT: www.ngdt.co.uk National Gamete Donation Trust, responsible for promoting embryo, egg and sperm donation in England and Wales

http://nuffieldbioethics.org/ Independent body advising on ethical issues relating to medical and biological research

www.ons.gov.uk Office for National Statistics – demographic information from the Census that is taken every ten years as well as from all other Government departments health, education, work & pensions.

Office of the Public Guardian: www.gov.uk/government/organisations/office-of the-public-guardian

www.prideangel.com an online service to share information about creating a family using donors, particularly but not exclusively LGBT. Connects donors, recipients and co-parents and provides advice and information. Free to join, donations welcome.

www.pinkfamilies.com US-based website with information on all aspects of family building and family life for LGBT people.
www.stonewall.org.uk/help-advice/parenting-rights Lesbian, gay, bi- and trans- sexual equality campaign, providing advice, information and support.

Taking Charge of Your Fertility: www.tcoyf.com

Turn2Us:www.turn2us.org.uk/Your-Situation/Bringing-up-a-child

Twins & Multiple Birth Association (TAMBA): www.tamba.org.uk/Support/One-Parent-Families The national (UK) organisations for multiple births – the website is excellent for information, and there are many local groups for support.

www.varta.org.au the State of Victoria (Australia)'s Assisted Reproduction Authority website. They are the world leaders in abolishing anonymity.

## Solo mum blogs and websites

http://attemptingsinglemotherhood.blogspot.co.uk
www.ellamentalmama.com
https://jannicamerrit.wordpress.com
http://jennandtate.blogspot.com
www.motherhoodreimagined.com - and Sarah Kowalski's YouTube channel:
www.youtube.com/watch?v=uynMAbIE3fo&t=10s
https://smcwannabe.com/about
https://thestorkandi.com
http://notbyaccident.net/
http://www.solomomtoadonorchild.com/blog/

## Beyond the UK – other European resources

**European-wide:**
http://donoroffspring.eu/

**Belgium**
www.co-parents.fr/legislation/lois-en-belgique.php

**Denmark**
www.facebook.com/Solomor.dk

**France**
www.co-parents.fr/La-PMA-pour-les-femmes-seules-en-France.php
www.parent-solo.fr
www.parent-solo.fr/dossier-722-maternites-solo-dominique-mehl.html

**Germany**
www.familienplanung.de/kinderwunsch/behandlung-im-ausland/gesetzliche-bestimmungen-im-ueberblick/
Although treating single women is now permitted in Germany, some sperm banks and fertility clinics do not accept single women as patients, so many travel north to Denmark where the systems are straight-forward and welcoming, or further away to Spain or Eastern Europe.

**Ireland**
www.solo.ie

**Italy**
A Blog:mammasingleperscelta.wordpress.com
www.smallfamilies.it/
www.associazione-oneparent.org

**Spain**
https://masola.org/author/rosa/
Asociación Madres Solteras por Elección:
https://madressolterasporeleccion.org/
https://maternidad.enfemenino.com/foro/chat-reproduccion-asistida-fd1030300

**Switzerland**
www.co-parents.fr/legislation/lois-en-suisse.php

## What others have said about this book

*"Going it Alone is a very thorough, practical, and readable guide to being a solo mom in the UK. It is packed with information based on both Engel's own personal experience and her long-time work with other solo moms. She covers almost every possible aspect of choosing to be a single mom in a thoughtful and sound fashion. It will both educate you and make you think, which makes it a must-read if you're thinking about becoming or are a solo mom, or just want to learn more about the subject."*

***Jane Mattes**, LCSW, Founder and Director: Single Mothers by Choice (SMC)*

*www.singlemothersbychoice.org*

:::::::::::::::::::::::

*"This is a wonderful, comprehensive and well-written resource for anyone considering solo motherhood as well as solo mums with children. Essential reading.*

***Nina Barnsley, Director, – DC Network***

:::::::::::::::::::::::

*"If, like me, you've had enough of society telling you that you can have it all, yet not producing the men to go with it, then this is the book for you.*

*Taking you step-by-step through the facts, stats and stages of becoming a solo mum by choice, this book puts to bed all the concerns around donor conception and helps you make the right choice for YOU!*

*Peppered with real life experiences that even your gran can relate to. Plus some great techniques for how to deal with the nosey parents at the school gates. If you're thinking of going it alone, stop thinking and start reading!"*

***Ellamental mama,*** *alternative solo mum blogger,* *www.ellamentalmama.com*

::::::::::::::::::::::

**Joni** on Amazon, 6 July 2019
Clearly-written & UK-focused, down-to-earth & comprehensive. Obviously thoroughly researched, with lots of references and mums' quotes.

::::::::::::::::::::::

**Rita Ferris-Taylor** in Good Reads Jul 16, 2019: This is a comprehensive and indispensable book!! Emily Engel has a wealth of direct personal experience, as well as many years of experience of supporting other solo mums in a range of circumstances. She is generous and sensitive in sharing her thoughts and tips, as well as including direct quotes from others with different views.

::::::::::::::::::::::

**Ali Jary on Amazon, 19 July 2019**
A really grounded resource for women thinking of parenting a child alone - full of information and advice covering every aspect from practicalities to emotional responses, examples and experiences from women who have taken this choice . Fantastic hand-holding .

ISBN 978-1-78926-720-4

Lightning Source UK Ltd.
Milton Keynes UK
UKHW022133120421
381871UK00011B/2838